Welcome to our third edition of Quintessentially Pure. It is with great excitement that we bring to you the latest collection of the most luxurious and stylish hotels and day spas from around the world. Each of the 100 featured properties has its own character and uniqueness and offers the highest quality treatments to respond to your individual wellness and beauty needs.

Given the many demands encountered in today's changing and challenging world, it has never been more important to nurture and care for oneself. Quintessentially Pure is designed to provide you with all of the options to consider when choosing the best spa experience for you. Whether your schedule allows for a simple day spa get-away or a longer, therapeutic escape, Pure has it all.

Quintessentially Pure is one title from a stunning collection of luxury books at Quintessentially Publishing. If you would like to find out more about the fantastic properties highlighted in this publication, please visit www.quintessentiallypure.com.

Coming soon, Quintessentially Reserve's fourth edition will be published in December and will feature the best 150 hotels worldwide. Quintessentially Living USA and Quintessentially Living Perfume books are scheduled for release in spring 2010. I hope you will enjoy this edition of Pure and will come to rely on it as a trusted resource for your wellness and beauty care.

Edward Rodwell
Director

Pure...

The spa concept is as old as civilisation itself. For thousands of years people have understood the importance of rest, relaxation and healing. In fact, the word originates from the Latin 'Sanitas Per Aqua', meaning 'health through water'. The Ancient Greeks, Romans and Egyptians were among the first civilisations to embrace the spa ethos. They believed that inner peace and balance play an important role in total body health. Over the millennia spas have evolved into genuine 'havens', places to go to seek refuge and escape from our stressful modern day lifestyles. The modern day spa is all this and so much more.

Here we find age-old traditional techniques handed down over the generations, as well as the most up to date, innovative methods of healing. But, equally important is the spa ritual; the journey we are taken on from the moment we enter. The spa experience nurtures and comforts us, gently easing away the tension and worries in our lives.

Spas are fast becoming not just a luxury, but a necessity in which we are able to treat both mind and body. They offer us the opportunity to find our true selves, to restore our inner balance and pamper our over-worked bodies. On ending the spa journey, we emerge feeling renewed, energised and refreshed, ready to face the world once more. The rise in spa popularity means that we can now enjoy the ever-improving quality of treatments in the most beautiful and opulent surroundings. The diversity of spas across the continents has never been greater than it is today, allowing us to experience the true meaning of luxury.

Quintessentially Pure invites you take your own spa journey. We have searched the globe to bring you the most beautiful, tranquil and luxuriously decadent spas the world has to offer. Take some time out for you... and enjoy.

Contents

Africa and Indian Ocean

Africa is often referred to as the 'mother land', the oldest inhabited territory on Earth and the place where human life began. It is the second largest of the continents, and the only one to span both the southern and northern temperate zones. Home to savannah plains, lush rainforest, arid desert and even snow-capped mountains; there is something here to suit all tastes, from the most adventurous traveller to the more discerning connoisseur.

Africa is the most ethnically diverse place in the world, with 53 countries and over 2,000 spoken languages. It has seen a rich and turbulent history, having been colonised many times over by both Europeans and Asians. Modern day Africa is exciting and vibrant, a place of contradictions.

The land is rich in natural resources, and African spa treatments make the most of the abundant plants and flowers. Lavender, perhaps the most well known of all the flowers used in health treatments, originates from these lands. It is most commonly used in the form of an essential oil, a highly concentrated and potent plant extract. Lavender has been used for centuries to calm allergic irritations, soothe damaged skin and to promote relaxation.

Shea butter is another popular African skin care ingredient. This moisturising butter is extracted from the shea nut, and used to treat dry skin conditions such as eczema and psoriasis. Rich in omega oils, it has been hailed as a miracle treatment for scars, and is used today all over the world.

The most luxurious and sought-after bounty of Africa has to be the famous argan oil. This precious oil is extracted from the nut of the argan tree by the Berber women of Morocco. A well kept secret until recent years, argan oil has been used for its anti-ageing and anti-oxidant properties on both the skin and the hair.

The tropical islands of the Indian Ocean are amongst the most beautiful and exotic in the world. Idyllic, powder soft beaches slope gently into turquoise seas, perfect for diving and snorkelling. Venture further inland to find lush, tropical jungle and picturesque waterfalls. The islands owe their fertile land to a volcanic history, and the mineral-rich soil is perfect for sustaining many tropical plants. They remain largely unspoilt, remote and secluded from the rest of the world. The reputation of these gems of the Indian Ocean is legendary; quite simply, they are paradise.

The Islands have a mixed history, colonised by the French, the Indian and the English. Many of the Islands still keep their French names, and evidence of the French culture remains in everyday life. The Indian culture also has an influence. One of the most common languages spoken is Hindi, and the Indian philosophies of Ayurveda and Yoga are widely used in the spa treatments

Ayurveda, meaning 'science of life', is an ancient Indian philosophy dating back to 4,000 BC. Ayurveda is a way of life, a code of practise designed to achieve total body health.

The method takes into account all aspects of life, including emotions and personality traits, to treat the person as a whole. Ayurvedic practitioners undergo years of study to learn the complex philosophy, and every treatment begins with a detailed consultation to determine the client's individual *dosha*. Ayurveda is not only deeply indulgent, but also highly effective in tackling many health conditions, including stress, digestive problems, and skin disorders.

From natural, organic treatments in remote and peaceful locations, to ultra chic urban spas, join us on a voyage of discovery throughout Africa and some of the most beautiful spas of the continent.

Africa and Indian Ocean

W Retreat & Spa-Maldives, AWAY® Spa, Fesdu Island, North Ari Atoll, Republic of Maldives
Tel: +960 666 2248 Email: away.spa@whotels.com Web: www.whotels.com/maldives

North Ari Atoll | Maldives

W Retreat & Spa-Maldives

This is the ultra-chic W Hotel's first retreat (two more are planned for Puerto Rico and Thailand). International DJs play at the underground nightclub, relaxed beats fill the air at the sassy over water bar and smiling staff are ever present to fulfill the US Brand's 'Whatever, Whenever' ethos. W Retreat & Spa–Maldives has brought a cutting-edge coolness to one of the region's most idyllic white-sand, tropical island hideaways. But, while bar and nightlife may be buzzing (all be it in comparison to the surrounding area), the primary purpose is relaxation and the award-winning AWAY® Spa provides it. Four indoor and shaded outdoor treatment areas are set above the brilliant turquoise waters. Each is totally private and equipped with aromatic steam room, sunken tub, rain shower and two massage tables. It's so romantic, couples often spend the entire afternoon having treatments and gazing out over the India Ocean, they may even order a post-treatment meal on the terrace. There are over 40 treatments to choose from including traditional Ayurvedic therapies, all personalised according to your individual dosha to bring physical, mental and emotional balance. The spa also offers Yoga and meditation on a teak-lined platform that floats above the island's spectacular house reef.

QUINTESSENTIALLY INSIDER
Experience the Shiatsu/Thai massage on a shaded day bed. You will sense ultimate freedom hovering over the ocean whilst surrendering to the 'magical hands' of the therapist - it will leave you revived and at ease…a perfect start to a day in paradise.

Jiva Grande Spa, Taj Exotica Resort & Spa, South Male Atoll, Republic of Maldives
Tel: +960 664 2200 Fax: +960 664 2211 Email: spaexotica.maldives@tajhotels.com Web: www.tajhotels.com

South Male Atoll | Maldives

Taj Exotica Resort and Spa

Jiva Grande Spa at the Taj Exotica Resort in the Maldives claims to be the first truly Indian spa outside India. Its design is based on Vastu principals (similar to Feng Shui, but rooted in Hinduism rather than Buddhism). And treatments celebrate India's ancient wellness heritage – in particularly the rituals enjoyed by Indian royalty throughout the centuries. The spa is accessed via a charming pergola located at the far end of the intimate private island resort. An array of picturesque spa pavilions fan out around a sandy courtyard, each one raised on stilts within the islands enormous sand lagoon. Three couple suites have private sundecks and bathtubs perfectly positioned to look out over the ocean. Soothing signature spa ceremonies, body therapies, heat experiences and authentic in-depth Ayurveda programmes can also be enjoyed at the Ayurveda pavilion. Guided Yoga and meditation is offered and, as befits any spa of great repute, unique spa cuisine – a new range of regenerative and antioxidant dishes based on Ayurvedic principles – is served on the relaxation deck.

QUINTESSENTIALLY INSIDER
For a unique experience try Alepa – the act of anointing the body. Offered at the lavish mud bath pavilion, it can be performed alone or as a couple (although a therapist is always on call) and is believed to honour the body, connecting you with the elements and your inner self or your loved one.

Anantara Spa at Naladhu, Velighandu Huraa, South Male Atoll, Republic of Maldives
Tel: +960 664 1888 Email: stay@naladhu.com Web: www.naladhu.com

South Male Atoll | Maldives

Anantara Spa at Naladhu

When it opened in March 2007, Naladhu Maldives, was named one of the world's hottest new resorts by *Condé Nast Traveller* (2007 Hot List). With just 19 totally private villas basking in unsurpassed luxury on a palm-fringed island, it is definitely one of the most exclusive. Bangkok-based architect Julian Coombs designed the weathered-wood villas to resemble much-loved holiday homes. With private gardens, hardwood decks, infinity-edge pools and outdoor eating *salas* they do not skimp on material comforts. Dedicated butlers attend to guest's every need and a team of spa professionals trained in various holistic healing traditions – Ayurveda, Thai, Balinese and more – will transform the villas into private spa retreats. Guests can choose from an extensive spa menu or indulge in specially devised programmes that incorporate the natural healing traditions of the islands: four-hand massages, herbal steams and *al fresco* floral baths to name a few. Gentle Yoga, breathing rituals and spa cuisine are also incorporated into daily agendas.

QUINTESSENTIALLY INSIDER
Treatments can take place in the comfort of your bedroom, in the shade of a towering palm on the beach or on your sun-bleached deck at twilight. But if you fancy a complete change of scene, embark on a spa journey that will literally transport you to three different islands within the emerald lagoon for three separate pampering experiences.

Hideaway Spa, Island Hideaway at Dhonakulhi Maldives, Spa Resort & Marina, Haa Alifu Atoll, North Maldives
Tel: +960 650 1515 Fax: +960 650 1616 Email: sales@island-hideaway.com Web: www.island-hideaway.com

Haa Alifu Atoll | Maldives

Island Hideaway at Dhonakulhi Maldives

If you're not planning to arrive at Island Hideaway Spa Resort by private jet, seaplane or yacht, you can expect the impeccable service to begin as soon as you step off the plane at Male' International Airport. Guests are whisked onto a connecting 50 minute scenic flight to Hanimaadhoo (you'll hardly have time make use of the business lounge at the disposal of all Island Hideaway guests), and then into a speedboat for an exhilarating 20-minute ride to the island. Your personal butler will guide you to your wonderfully secluded private villa, one of 43 on this idyllic island of lush vegetation and white sandy beaches. Despite the space and range of facilities offered, only five per cent of the 1.4km long island has been developed, leaving the remainder in its pristine natural state. The Hideaway Spa embraces this dramatic location, echoing the ocean and nature, in the design of its private spa areas – two Lagoon Spa Pavilions with private ocean views and four Spa Land Villas. Internal waterways, waterfall walls and feature sand floors are combined with natural stone, teak furnishings and silk fabrics. The 'sun, sand and sea' theme is also apparent in the comprehensive spa menu, which offers treatments including the Sun Soother Wrap, Ocean Detox Wrap or Hideaway Sand Massage, as well as more traditional Asian favourites and Elemis therapies.

QUINTESSENTIALLY INSIDER
If it's total seclusion you're after, stay at one of the two Hideaway Water Suites erected on wooden stilts in the shallow turquoise-blue lagoon. Each villa has its own exclusive ocean-view treatment room, sauna, steam room and round bathtub outside on the deck.

Shanti Ananda Maurice, Rivière des Galets, Chemin Grenier, Maurice, Mauritius
Tel: +230 603 7200 Fax: +230 603 7250 E-mail: reservation@shantiananda.mu Web: www.shantiananda.com

Maurice | Mauritius

Shanti Ananda Maurice

Shanti Ananda on the wild and beautiful southern coast of Mauritius is the tropical outpost of the award-winning Himalayan retreat, Ananda, and the island's first destination spa. Surrounded by lush green hills, turquoise waters and an inviting sandy beach, this exotic destination is a perfect blend of an intimate escape, a relaxed, fun-filled getaway and a luxurious spa retreat. Twenty-five treatment rooms are beautifully laid out around landscaped water gardens with specialised areas for each spa discipline. Ananda fans will recognise the emphasis on Ayurveda and Yoga and also the team of experienced consultants, spa therapists, nutritionists and personal trainers whose combined expertise provides guidance for a healthier lifestyle. Facilities include an infinity-edge pool overlooking the Indian Ocean, tennis courts, a separate saltwater pool for Watsu treatments, a heated lap-pool, Yoga pavilions, a glass-sided gym surrounded by jungle foliage and an enchanting tea pavilion. Activities, ranging from golf to water sports and exciting treks, are available for the asking. Accommodation outshines even that at the original property and the cuisine offers personalised menus specially devised to suit every palate.

QUINTESSENTIALLY INSIDER
The spiritually inclined should ask for a Yogi 'havan' ceremony – an ancient Indian fire ritual performed just for you in a secluded spot on the beach. While adventurous holiday-makers can sample a host of exciting escapes and special packages on offer.

23

Maradiva Spa, Maradiva Villas Resort & Spa, Wolmar, Mauritius
Tel: +230 403 1500 Fax: +230 453 5555 Email: info@maradiva.com Web: www.maradiva.com

Wolmar | Mauritius

Maradiva Villas Resort & Spa

Previously managed by Taj Hotels and Resorts, Maradiva Villas Resort and Spa is a paradise of luxurious, peaceful delight and certainly one of the finest resorts in Mauritius. Enveloped by majestic mountains on an expansive tree-shaded beach, vast colonial style villas (we're talking between 163 and 345 metre sq each) with private pools and terraces gaze out over the turquoise lagoon of Tamarin Bay. With butler service, Bose surround sound systems, walled-garden showers and Nespresso coffee makers, no detail has been overlooked. The same can be said for the resort's spa which takes its spiritual inspiration from India; the philosophies of ancient eastern wellness techniques are beautifully combined with a welcoming Mauritian charm. Authentic in-depth Ayurveda programme are administered under the guidance of Vaidyas (Ayurveda physicians) in two dedicated Ayurvedic treatment suites. A further four treatment suites have private gardens and immense carved stone tubs. In preference to the use of commercial products, spa therapists create unique blends using natural ingredients and 100% essential oils. Guests may relax in the shade of bougainvilleas or the orange scented heat of the laconium, refresh under outdoor tropical showers and revitalise in the open-air cascade pool. There is also a Yoga-meditation pavilion where trained instructors and healers conduct regular sessions, a hammam, a samarium (sauna-steam room combo) and a traditional beauty salon.

QUINTESSENTIALLY INSIDER
For direct access to the expansive tree-shaded Wolmar beach, request one of the 11 Beachfront Villa's. These also have an option to interconnect with another villa, perfect for small groups or families.

25

Royal Palm Spa by Clarins, Royal Palm, Grand Baie, Mauritius
Tel: +44 207 408 5025 Fax: +44 207 408 5029 Email: concierge@theroyalpalm.co.uk Web: www.beachcomber-hotels.co.uk/uk

Grand Baie | Mauritius

Royal Palm

The flagship of the Mauritian owned Beachcomber Hotels Group and the most prestigious address in the Indian Ocean, Royal Palm, unveiled a fresh new spa by Clarins in October 2007. It is one of the best on the island. The spa is set in the hotel's soothing tropical gardens amidst the sound of gently flowing water and the scent of sweet frangipani flowers. Simple and elegant in design, it is laid out around a pool and large sundeck, and its use of natural materials – lava stone, granite, wood and slate – blends harmoniously with the lush surroundings. Floor-to-ceiling windows blur the line between indoors and out and treatment cabins – some single, some double and some with whirlpool baths – open onto walled gardens and private patios. Facilities include two Ayurvedic rooms plus rooms dedicated to reiki, Thai massage and balneotherapy. Highly trained therapists offer a full range of Clarins spa and beauty treatments as well as a variety of different massages and holistic therapies, all tailored to individual needs. There is also a Yoga pavilion and an adjacent sports centre offering the latest in fitness equipment kinesis, power plates, Pilates, personal trainers, squash, tennis and private coaching.

QUINTESSENTIALLY INSIDER
Book the hotel's Rolls Royce Phantom (the only one on the island) for your transfers to and from the airport. Or if you can't bear the one hours drive – opt for the helicopter.

Shiseido Spa, Spa de Constance, Constance Ephelia Resort, Port Launay, Mahé, Seychelles
Tel: +230 402 2770 Fax: +230 402 2616 Email: resaeurope@constancehotels.com Web: www.epheliaresort.com

Spa de Constance

One to watch out for in 2010 is the Constance Ephélia Resort, the second property in the Seychelles (after Constance Lémuria Resort on Praslin) from the luxury Indian Ocean-based Constance Hotels Experience group. Scheduled to open in February, Constance Ephélia Resort will gaze out over the marine national park of Port Launay from one of the most beautiful and un-spoilt beaches on Mahé. The huge 300-acre property will feature 267 suites and villas designed in harmony with the surroundings and spread out among lush vegetation. Ten one-bedroom spa villas with en-suite treatment areas will be set in the beautiful tropical garden environment of the Spa Village creating a wellness destination in itself. Treatments and products will be from award-winning Japanese brand Shiseido and the highlight will be the striking Shiseido Pavilion with three treatment rooms devoted to Shiseido's Qi method of total wellbeing. Further facilities from the Spa de Constance will include another 11 treatment rooms (one for couples and two exclusively for facial treatments), a Yoga pavilion, sauna, Jacuzzi, beauty salons and two pools.

QUINTESSENTIALLY INSIDER
This is a place where you can take the kids too. An all day kids club will cater for children aged 4-12, babysitters are available on request and even the restaurants will whip up some gourmet toddler treats.

Rock Spa, Frégate Island Private, Seychelles
Tel: +248 670 100 Fax: +248 670 900 Email: spa@fregate.com/ reservations@fregate.com Web: www.fregate.com

Frégate Island Private | Seychelles

The Rock Spa

The ultimate luxury eco-retreat, Frégate Island Private, has just 16 secluded villas and one Presidential Villa accommodating only a selected number of guests at any one time. The island is an environmentalist's paradise; teeming with native flora it is home to many rare birds, giant tortoises and the rare Seychelles terrapin, which once numbered only eight individuals but whose population has been nurtured back to over 100 today. This is the ideal place, therefore, to enjoy nature's remedies. The resort's Rock Spa – so called because of its dramatic approach via a rock archway and a canyon of granite boulders – eschews the commercialism of branded spa products in favour of natural, locally grown preparations. In the Rock Spa's own apothecary Madame Dibwa (derived from the Creole for 'the fairy woman from the forest') blends indigenous know-how with the principles of herbalism and aromatherapy to create unique scrubs, pastes and oils. These form the basis of traditional treatments for relaxation, revitalisation, detoxification and specific ailments. Performed from the Rock Spa's cliff top plateau before panoramic sea views and flanked with waterfalls, it is a spa experience that truly embraces nature and this unique location.

QUINTESSENTIALLY INSIDER
Ask for Villa 16 for spectacular views from the private infinity-edge pool across the white sand Anse Macquereau beach towards Praslin and La Digue. With its own mini-spa it represents the ultimate in private pampering.

Sainte Anne Spa by Clarins, Sainte Anne Resort & Spa, Seychelles
Tel: +44 207 408 5020 Fax: +44 207 408 5029 Email: info@bchot.co.uk Web: www.beachcomber-hotels.co.uk/uk

Sainte Anne | Seychelles

Sainte Anne Resort & Spa

A short 15 minute boat ride from the main island of Mahé, Sainte Anne is a 500-acre private island; home to lush forests, sandy coves and an all-villa luxury resort. The effortlessly elegant Sainte Anne Resort & Spa is set between powder-like beaches and its own magnificent gardens. Among the exotic frangipane trees, bougainvilleas, hibiscuses and palm trees is the newly refurbished spa by Clarins – it is all part of the Sainte Anne experience. A Japanese-style entrance leads to a slate-tiled pool and eight elegant massage cabins. All wood, stone and tranquil reflection pools, the natural materials blend beautifully with the exotic vegetation. Facilities include a Yoga room, a balneotherapy room, two saunas, two hammams and a beauty parlour. Clarins treatments combine the natural benefits of active botanical extracts with highly trained therapists – a marriage of effective products and expert techniques that will leave guests feeling refreshed and relaxed.

QUINTESSENTIALLY INSIDER
Sainte Anne Resort & Spa is right at the heart of one of the most beautiful marine parks in the Indian Ocean. Take the opportunity to explore and discover the incredible diversity of life in the warm and clear Seychelles water.

U-Spa Barrière, Hotel & Ryads Naoura Barrière, Djebel Alakhdar bab doukkala, Marrakech Médina, Morocco
Tel: +212 524 459 040 Fax: +212 524 459 001 Email: risinaoura@lucienbarriere.com Web: www.naoura-barriere.com

U-Spa Barrière

Lucien Barrière (The deluxe French group behind Paris' Fouquet's restaurant and the legendary Casino Montreux) opened Naoura Barrière, its first hotel outside France, early this year. Bringing a touch of French *art de vivre* to culturally rich and fashionable Marrakech, the hotel is already a cult address. Ideally situated in a five-acre garden plot at the heart of the bustling Médina, the hotel and spa is an oasis of peace. Set under summery palms around a majestic open-air pool, the U-Spa Barrière is flooded with natural light from a central glass roof. Boasting two Morrocan hammams with separate rooms for traditional black soap massage, relaxation and steam, as well as an aquatic wellbeing circuit (unique in Marrakech) and a state-of-the-art gym, this is the cities leading wellness spot. A range of treatments performed from eight treatment booths use natural oriental cosmetics brand, Les Sens de Marrakech (distributed via exclusive outlets throughout Europe and the East).

QUINTESSENTIALLY INSIDER

For an authentic Marrakech experience stay in one of the Hotel's exceptional Ryads. Nestled among white flowers and garden greenery they each feature between three and six bedrooms, two lounges (one with a fireplace), a fitted kitchen, terrace and a private pool.

The Spa at Cape Grace, V&A Waterfront, Cape Town, South Africa
Tel: +27 21 410 7140 Fax: +27 21 419 7622 Email: spa@capegrace.com Web: www.capegrace.com

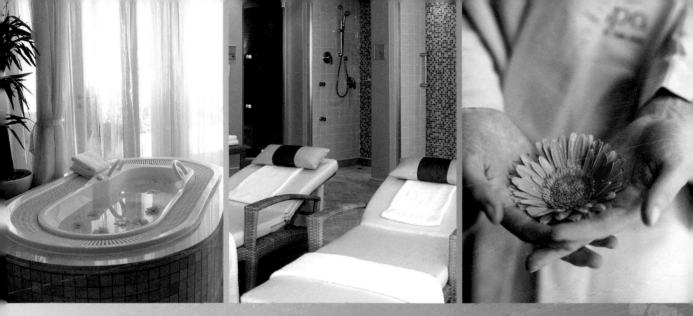

Cape Town | South Africa

Ever wondered what an African Knopkierie massage would feel like? Indigenous spa therapies are in vogue offering an inspired way for jet-setters to relax and connect with their destination. At Cape Grace, it is the cultures of the South African people, the flora of the continent and its traditional remedies that have influenced the hotel's exclusive spa. Zulu Knopkierie sticks form part of the Thaba Massage Treatment, the African Cape Massage draws on the circular massage techniques of the *Khoi San* (South Africa's desert dwelling hunters) and the Africology hydrating facial uses locally harvested ingredients (African potato immune booster, rooibos tea and shea butter). Located on the top floor of the hotel, superb panoramic views across the peninsula are another excellent reason to visit. Cape Grace is nestled on a private quay between Cape Town's bustling Waterfront and the international yacht marina. Surrounded by water on three sides, seals frolic below and seagulls soar above. The hotel also offers a heated outdoor swimming pool, a well stocked library, a superb restaurant, and a sophisticated bar with an incredible selection of single malt whiskies.

QUINTESSENTIALLY INSIDER
Venture out on the hotel's privately owned 56-foot luxury motor yacht at sunset and enjoy an exclusive massage treatment on deck followed by refreshing sundowners.

The Sanctuary Spa, The Twelve Apostles Hotel, Camps Bay, Cape Peninsula, South Africa
Tel: +27 21 437 9000 Fax: +27 21 437 9001 Email: info@thesanctuaryspa.co.za Web: www.12apostleshotel.com

The Twelve Apostles Hotel

The Sanctuary Spa at The Twelve Apostles Hotel has an enviable location; just 15 minutes drive (or a short helicopter hop) from the city centre and V&A Waterfront, situated in the tranquillity of The Table Mountain National Park. The award-winning subterranean spa (the third best Hotel Spa in Africa, Middle East and Indian Ocean Islands according to *Condé Nast Traveller* Spa Awards 2007) is dug deep into the rock, just a few metres from the azure waters of the Atlantic Ocean. This atmospheric underground grotto is where the discerning traveller can indulge and be pampered or prepare for a bikini-clad afternoon on fashionable Camps Bay beach nearby. Facilities are fantastic and it's certainly possible to spend half a day lounging in the large Jacuzzi, chilling in the plunge pools, drifting in the flotation pool or smearing on mud in Cape Town's only Rasul chamber. There are seven treatment rooms including state-of-the-art hydrotherapy facilities and a Vichy shower. But to appreciate the spa's incredible setting opt for an ocean view treatment in one of the new glass gazebos planted amongst the *fynbos* on the mountainside. *Fynbos* is the hardy vegetation typical of the region, and the spa's Moya product range (a Western Cape based brand) uses essential oils, created from the *fynbos* plants, in its 100% natural lotions and creams.

QUINTESSENTIALLY INSIDER
Fynbos also features at the hotel's Azure restaurant. Executive Chef Roberto de Carvalho has found international acclaim with his innovative menu infused with *fynbos* herbs – enjoy this, as well as the restaurant's panoramic views, after a session in the spa.

Chem Chem AMANI Spa, Chem Chem Tarangire, Tanzania
Tel: +255 782 322 000 Email: reservations@chemchemsafari.com Web: www.chemchemsafari.com

Chem Chem Tarangire | Tanzania

Chem Chem

Chem Chem Tarangire is ideally set between the vast plains and forests of Tarangire National Park and the bird-rich waters of Lake Manyara in Tanzania. An advocate of what they call the 'slow safari'©, here it is not just about the excitement of spotting a rhino from a 4x4 (although that may be part of it) it is about experiencing Africa in a more relaxed manner. A calming holistic massage under the bows of an acacia tree, a stroll around the lake with a knowledgeable guide, a private picnic, sleeping out under an unfamiliar night sky, a lesson in wildlife photography or Swahili cooking: Chem Chem is about slowing down and enjoying a new perspective. The excellent AMANI spa is central to this philosophy offering healing treatments designed to help guests put the brakes on and connect with nature. Products from holistic body and skin care brand ILA are created to retain and transmit natural energy from the pure organic ingredients. The use of water, fire, stone and wood throughout the camps and lodges creates fluency with the environment and further enhances the African experience. And the large outdoor pool and sun terrace is perfect for kicking back with a glass of chilled wine and observing surrounding abundant wildlife.

QUINTESSENTIALLY INSIDER
Enjoy a magical massage on a platform surrounded by palm trees – a feature at all eight elegant suite-style tents. Ask for tent number one or eight for most privacy.

41

Asia and the Pacific

The immense continent of Asia covers a staggering 30% of the world's land mass. It is a place of extremes – from the highest mountains to the lowest depressions, the driest deserts to the wettest lowlands, tropical heat to arctic cold. The individual regions are separated by vast, impassable landscapes, and each civilisation has developed in its own unique way.

Asia is a land of huge religious diversity; a spiritual place infused with mythology, architectural wonders and sacred spaces. The land flourishes with precious plants and flowers offering huge health benefits. Spa treatments focus on both the spiritual and the natural with a desire to achieve complete physical and mental wellbeing. Drawing inspiration from ancient traditions they have a great respect for the natural world.

Green China Tea, a widely known health drink, was discovered here. The tea is rich in anti-oxidants, making it a true elixir to counteract our toxin-rich modern lifestyle. Extracts of this 'super plant' are used in oils, creams and lotions and applied to the skin to prevent the signs of ageing.

Himalayan salts, ethically mined in the foothills of this colossal mountain range, are rich in precious minerals. They are used in baths and scrubs to boost circulation, re-mineralise the body and help balance dry skin conditions.

There are literally hundreds of islands dotted around the Pacific Ocean, each unique and beautiful in its own way. The vast majority are 'hot spots', created from ancient volcanic eruptions. They have never been in contact with any of the continental plates, and have evolved separately from the rest of the world.

The Pacific Islands boast a year-round tropical climate, miles of pristine sandy beaches, and crystal clear waters. They are exceptionally well preserved, with no real mass tourism, making them ideal getaways for travellers looking to find peace and quiet.

Some of the rarest species of plants and flowers grow exclusively in this part of the world and the local people have embraced them whole heartedly. Combining ancient practises with native plants, the Pacific Islanders have created a diverse range of health treatments.

Perhaps the most widely used ingredient of the Pacific is the guava fruit. Its numerous properties make it a hero in skincare. The leaves contain an effective yet gentle anti-bacterial agent, perfect for oily skins. The fruit is rich in vitamins, particularly vitamin C, needed for collagen and elastin. High in carotenoids and minerals, it also provides powerful antioxidant and antihistamine effects.

Lomi Lomi, simply meaning 'massage' in Polynesian, is a refreshingly different form of hands on therapy originating from this region. Using continuous flowing strokes to gently yet deeply nurture the body, there is no set format; it is a spiritual process which involves the practitioner working intuitively with the receiver, therefore no two massages will be identical.

Balinese massage is a form of Indonesian therapy that is as varied as it is effective. Fusing together reflexology, aromatherapy, acupressure and Thai massage, it is a rigorous and luxurious treatment. The Balinese massage is performed with a deep pressure designed to work on strained muscles and joints and is ideal for those wishing to experience a multitude of Asian spa treatments in one.

We are pleased to offer you a wonderfully diverse selection of the most aspirational spas in Asia and the Pacific. Our collection offers a taste of the old and the new, combining ancient traditions with modern innovations for an unforgettable spa experience.

Talise Spa at Madinat Jumeirah, Dubai, United Arab Emirates
Tel: +971 43 666 818 Fax: +971 43 666 800 Email: mj-talise@jumeirah.com Web: www.madinatjumeirah.com

Dubai | UAE

Madinat Jumeirah

Dubai is no place for moderation and the magnificent 874-room beachfront Madinat Jumeirah resort does not hold back. It is styled to resemble an ancient Arabian citadel with meandering waterways, courtyard summerhouses and traditional souks. Guests are transported around the resort and the two kilometres of private beach in traditional *abras* (water taxis). With views over ancient Arabian wind towers as well as the stunning sail-shaped icon that is the neighbouring Burj Al Arab, the effect is enchanting. The resort's Talise Spa is similarly impressive. One of the best in the region, it comprises of 26 individual treatment villas designed in island clusters amidst secluded waterways and tropical gardens. There is also a hammam, sauna, steam room and icy cold plunge pool. The treatment list is huge and offers more than just a pampering experience. Indulgent spa therapies are plentiful as are the ancient rituals imported from around the world. But more inspiring alternative therapies – such as the popular Chakra Balancing Therapy (a combination of massage, essential oils, crystals and visualisation techniques) – plus nutritional guidance, Yoga and meditation are intended to take guests on a path of self-discovery.

QUINTESSENTIALLY INSIDER
Brides to be should try out the Bridal Ritual Shiffa Hammam Ancienne, an ancient Middle Eastern experience that will deeply cleanse and soften your skin, balancing your energy and leaving you feeling revitalised and wonderfully rested ahead of the big day.

Ananda in the Himalayas, The Palace Estate, Narendra Nagar, Tehri Garhwal, Uttarakhand, India
Tel: +91 137 822 7500 Fax: +91 137 822 7550 Email: sales@anandaspa.com Web: www.anandaspa.com

Ananda in the Himalayas

Ananda has been voted 'World's number one destination spa' by *Condé Nast Traveller* for three consecutive years. It perfectly combines the serene ambiance of the Himalayan foothills and the ancient practices of Ayurveda with luxurious accommodation and advanced international therapies. Set on a mountain ridge around a former Maharaja's palace, Ananda looks out over the sacred river Ganges and the holy valley of Rishikesh (The Beetles 1960's spiritual destination). There are more than 80 different treatments on offer including massage, beauty therapies, Ayurvedic rituals and a new range of Tibetan healing therapies unique to Ananda. Guests are nurtured and directed by a team of consultants, qualified nutritionists and experienced therapists who devise programmes specific to individual needs and health goals. The retreat is dedicated to restoring balance and harmony through a holistic approach and Yoga plays a significant role in this. Intricately designed open-air Yoga pavilions are set among the Himalayan flowerbeds, tranquil water features and strolling peacocks of the estate's lush hillside gardens. The spa also features hydrotherapy facilities, an outdoor temperature-controlled lap-pool, a state-of-the-art gymnasium and a show kitchen where chefs instruct guests in how to make Ananda's wholesome Ayurvedic cuisine.

QUINTESSENTIALLY INSIDER
Ananda's most luxurious accommodation comes within the palace itself – the spectacular Viceregal suite with its own rooftop terrace and Jacuzzi overlooking the valley. Alternatively, the one- and two-bedroom Ananda Villas include private pools and saunas.

Rambagh Palace

Rambagh Palace, home to generations of Royals in the centre of bustling Jaipur, was converted into a luxury hotel in 1957. From the white marble verandas to the ballrooms and the sweeping lawns, this lavish sprawl offers guests a taste of regal life. The newly launched Jiva Grande Spa is set in two exquisite tented pavilions, recreations of the beautiful Mughal encampments of the 16th and 17th centuries. Each one unfolds a spacious and completely private couples suite embellished with wooden floors, glowing chandeliers, copper soak tubs and Indian love swings. Wet areas include an outdoor Jacuzzi, two traditional Finnish saunas (with special stoves for heating aromatic peridodit stones) and a steam bath with fibre optic lighting. The new outdoor pool is large and impressive, but the original stone and marble indoor swimming pool, specially created for Her Highness of Jaipur, is of a splendour that is not often matched. The spa menu draws on the ancient wellness heritage of India and treatments use only natural products derived from Indian herbs and essential oils.

QUINTESSENTIALLY INSIDER
Experience the inherent powers of Jaipur's famed gemstones. Dr. Chauhan, an eminent alternative therapist, will help you achieve peace, happiness, health and wealth by combining gem therapy with an individual's unique vibration.

Rambagh Palace, Jaipur, Bhawani Singh Road, Jaipur , India
Tel: +91 141 221 1919 Fax: +91 141 238 5098 Email: sparbp.jaipur@tajhotels.com Web: www.tajhotels.com

Himachal Pradesh | India

Wildflower Hall

From its magnificent perch atop a densely forested ridge, Wildflower Hall looks out over misty valleys in the foothills of the Himalayas. The elegant 85-room Oberoi resort is built on the grounds of Lord Kitchener's former summer residence – this is where the commander-in-chief of the British forces in India came to relax and escape the summer heat. Interiors ooze old world charm and the tranquil ambience of a stately mountain retreat is apparent at the resort's fabulous Oberoi Spa. Breathtaking views from the indoor heated pool, outdoor heated whirlpool and Spa Suites extend across the valley to the distant mountains – best enjoyed as the sun sets on the snowy peaks. For those who prefer the soothing seclusion of the forest, two Spa Pavilions are set apart from the resort among the fragrant pine and cedar trees. Ayurvedic principals are combined with aromatherapy and western techniques to offer an impressive range of holistic spa therapies. Meanwhile the adventurous can trek, mountain bike, horse ride or river raft in the resort's 22 acres of virgin forest and beyond.

QUINTESSENTIALLY INSIDER
Ask for a private Yoga or meditation session in a forest clearing – the only sound apart from your breathing will be the whisper of wind, the rustle of leaves and the songs of birds.

Wildflower Hall, Shimla in the Himalayas, An Oberoi Resort, Chharabra, Shimla, Himachal Pradesh, India
Tel: +91 177 264 8585 Fax: +91 177 264 8686 Email: reservations.tufl@oberoihotels.com Web: www.wildflowerhall.com

Devi Garh, Serena Spa, Delwara - NH 8, Near Eklingji, Udaipur, Rajasthan, India
Tel: +91 295 328 9211-20 Fax: +91 295 330 4135 Email: devigarh@deviresorts.com Web: www.deviresorts.com

Rajasthan | India

Devi Garh

Far away from the stresses of the city in the ancient Aravali Hills near Udaipur, Devi Garh (acclaimed by *Condé Nast Traveller* and *Tatler* among others) is a perfect place to soothe the body, stimulate the mind and strengthen the spirit. The 39-all-suite property is a stunning heritage Rajput fort palace complete with towering sandstone walls, peaceful courtyards and a multitude of turrets. After years of restoration the interiors have been re-invented (courtesy of the best young designers in India), they are modern, clean-lined and minimalist. The effect is intensely calming and yet uniquely Indian. Serena Spa has a similar confluence of the historic and the contemporary. Therapists from Kerala combine traditional Ayurvedic treatments using medicated oils and herbal pastes with modern international spa concepts created by the all-natural skin care brand Decléor, Paris. Guests may experience a *kalari* (South Indian martial art) inspired Marma Massage in which the body is massaged by feet and hands followed by a traditional herbal body scrub, or a hot stone massage performed with naturally smoothed and energized river stones from Karnataka.

QUINTESSENTIALLY INSIDER
Don't miss the Yoga and meditation sessions which take place on the palace ramparts at sunrise.

Uma Paro, Paro, Bhutan
Tel: +975 827 1597 Fax: +975 827 1513 Email: res.paro@uma.como.bz Web: www.uma.paro.como.bz

Paro | Bhutan

Uma Paro

COMO Shambala Retreat at Christina Ong's singularly stylish Uma Paro is Bhutan's first significant holistic wellness spa. The entire nation is Buddhist with a deep respect for religious tradition; at Uma Paro the local culture and spirituality therefore forms a vital part of the wellness experience. The Retreat's facilities make use of its inspiring hilltop location. The Yoga studio overlooks the Paro Valley and can be opened up to catch mountain breezes. There is an indoor pool with a lovely outdoor sundeck and, in the pine forest, a 90metre-sq hot stone bath house which includes a private massage room for couples. Here, guests can indulge in the traditional Bhutanese Hot Stone Bath, a powerful stress reliever. Other therapies range from specific body treatments to facials and sophisticated massages, including some therapies using herbal remedies known to the ancient Buthanese system of natural healthcare. Experienced practitioners are confident enough to customise treatments according to individual needs and there is particular emphasis on Ayurveda. Cuisine is organic and health-giving, while excursions to monasteries, temples, villages and festivals provide intelligent, active access to Bhutanese life and the breathtaking landscape.

QUINTESSENTIALLY INSIDER
The COMO Shambhala approach to holistic wellness also encourages time away from the spa to experience both physical and cultural activities. The Adventure Retreat series at Uma Paro supports this philosophy with mountain biking across Bhutan, trekking to the foothills of Mt Jhomalhari and visits to remote *dzongs* and monasteries.

Amanpuri, Pansea Beach, Phuket, Thailand
Tel: +66 76 324 333 Fax: +66 76 324 100 Email: amanpuri@amanresorts.com Web: www.amanresorts.com

Phuket | Thailand

Amanpuri

Aman's flagship, the ultra-exclusive Amanpuri (a fave get-away for A-list celebs) on Phuket Island, is also home to Amanresorts' first full service spa. Aman Spa is located adjacent to the main resort in a secluded coconut grove overlooking the Andaman Sea. Six authentically Thai treatment pavilions are sprinkled among the palms. Each pavilion is a huge light-filled space of wood and glass with its own steam room, shower, bathtub and private meditation *sala*. Treatments are based on traditional Thai remedies and holistic therapies all using Aman's own product range – handmade with essential oils derived from wild plants and herbs. Other spa facilities include a sauna room, a granite steam room, six floodlit tennis courts, a floor-to-ceiling glass-walled gym and a fountain terrace where quietly attentive staff will whip up a refreshing health drink. High on the hillside two open-sided teakwood *sulas* provide the setting for dawn yoga and meditation sessions. A striking midnight-blue tiled pool is set below and sweeping steps cascade down to the idyllic crescent beach and a second 20 metre lap-pool.

QUINTESSENTIALLY INSIDER
Accommodation at Amanpuri is sublime; 40 architect-design stand-alone pavilions and 30 private villas interspersed throughout the coconut plantation. Ask for pavilions 105 or 103 for postcard perfect views of the teal-blue sea.

Anantara Phuket Resort and Spa, 888 Moo, 3 Tumbon Mai Khao, Amphur Thalang Phuket, Thailand
Tel: +66 76 336 100 Fax: +66 76 336 177 Email: phuket@anantara.com Web: www.anantara.com

Phuket | Thailand

Anantara Phuket

The latest spa experience from the acclaimed Anantara group opened on Phuket's still blissfully serene Mai Kao Beach last year. Anantara Spa Phuket is defined by the beauty and symbolism of the lotus flower – one of the Eight Auspicious Symbols of Buddhism, it represents enlightenment, rebirth and self-regeneration. Age-old massage techniques, aromatic elixirs made from natural local ingredients and an environment of complete serenity are intended to guide guests towards renewed physical and spiritual wellbeing. The resort is set in magnificent Bill Bensley-designed tropical gardens around a man-made lagoon. Eighty-three villas with souring wooden roofs mimic a traditional southern Thai water village. Each villa features a small sparkling swimming pool, an outdoor bathtub and a large day bed – ideal for in-villa Thai massages. The spa features eight spacious treatment suites all beautifully appointed with contemporary Thai decor and high thatched ceilings. Some feature terrazzo soaking tubs, others have Ayurveda and steam facilities. There is also a private Thai *sala* for alfresco massage, Yoga or meditation.

QUINTESSENTIALLY INSIDER
Help eliminate potential illnesses with a signature Meridian Lines massage. A deep relaxing massage is combined with reflexology to achieve a smooth flow of energy, or *prana*, thus enabling your body to reach optimum condition.

Anumba Spa, The Racha, Racha Yai Island, Phuket , Thailand
Tel: +66 76 355 455 Fax: +66 76 355 637 Email: reservations@theracha.com Web: www.theracha.com

Phuket | Thailand

Anumba Spa

Those who may consider Thailand's west coast around Phuket and Krabi a little overdeveloped should think again; the tiny Racha Yai Island 20 km off Phuket (Just 45 minutes from Phuket's International airport) offers complete seclusion as well as impossibly beautiful beaches and views across one of Thailand's most spectacular bays. The Racha is the islands glamorous yet unpretentious refuge. Seventy modern, clean-edged villas with Zen-like interiors dot the verdant hillside. The resort's Anumba Spa, just up from the pristine white beach, celebrates its privileged location amid soothing water gardens and towering palms with outdoor rain showers and open air massage pavilions. The philosophy is that of nature and renewed life. Treatments nourish the body with a range of natural products utilising flowers, herbs and oils from the lush surroundings. There are nine chic treatment rooms with plunge tubs and steam rooms plus a full-range gym and Yoga studio. Dazzling views of the mountains, the blue sky and the turquoise waters of the Andamon Sea enhance the feeling of total wellbeing.

QUINTESSENTIALLY INSIDER
After a day on the beach book in for a signature Thai Flower Ritual. A traditional Thai Herbal Scrub and floral bath is followed by a full body massage and Anumba Visible Brilliance Facial. This wonderful treatment, suitable for sensitive or sunburned skin, leaves you feeling refreshed and alive.

Four Seasons Resort Koh Samui, 219 Moo 5, Tambon Angthong, Koh Samui, Thailand
Tel: +66 77 243 000 Fax: +66 77 243 002 Email: spa.kohsamui@fourseasons.com Web: www.fourseasons.com/kohsamui

Koh Samui | Thailand

Four Seasons Resort Koh Samui

Koh Samui has established itself as Thailand's self-improvement Mecca with a keen respect for the holistic approach, Yogic lifestyle and detox culture. Four Seasons Resort Koh Samui on the Island's northern shore encompasses all these factors in a stunning Bill Bensley-designed retreat. Set on a forested hillside, the spa comprises five totally private tree-house inspired villas. Each one offers a choice of indoor or outdoor treatments, open-air bath rituals, natural rain shower or herbal steam bath whilst surrounded by the gentle and calming sights and sounds of the forest. The exceptional setting is intended to help guests re-connect with nature and the spa philosophy is that of total wellbeing – physical, emotional and spiritual. The menu combines centuries old healing techniques and rituals derived from Thai and other Asian cultures. Using the Just Pure range of organic, chemical-free spa products – hand made on specific days of the lunar month – many of the treatments are associated with moon phases (waning moon, new moon, waxing moon, full moon) which apparently have a critical influence on emotional and physical being. The spa also offers an alternative therapy menu designed to address spiritual needs.

QUINTESSENTIALLY INSIDER
Start the day with a dawn Yoga session led by the resort's resident Yogi at the beautiful ocean-view pavilion.

THE BARAI, 91 Khao-Takiap Road, Hua Hin, Prachuap Khiri Khan, Thailand
Tel: +66 32 511 234 Fax: +66 32 521 233 Email: thebarai.hrhuahin@hyatt.com Web: www.thebarai.com

Hua Hin | Thailand

THE BARAI

THE BARAI at Hua Hin is an award-winning destination spa located on four-and-a-half acres of serene beachfront land. Eight indulgent residential spa suites have luxurious oversized beds, spa treatment areas and large soaking tubs. There are also 18 individual treatment rooms for the use of day spa visitors. Designed by the renowned Thai architect and interior designer Mr. Lek Bunnag, THE BARAI is inspired by the cultural heritage of this region. His pioneering concept, intended to create moods and elicit an emotional response, has produced a haven of tranquillity and spirituality totally sheltered from the world outside. A highlight is the peaceful and secluded Tranquillity Court with a 30 metre-long swimming channel and breathtaking views of the Gulf of Thailand – ideal for Yoga, meditation and quiet contemplation. Treatments are based on the Thai belief of maintaining the vitality and balance of the four elements: water, earth, air and fire. Well-trained therapists use an abundance of fresh natural ingredients together with a selection of high-end, results driven spa products. THE BARAI is adjacent to the Hyatt Regency Hua Hin, which means that guests can also enjoy the facilities of the hotel including a large swimming pool, fitness centre and restaurants.

QUINTESSENTIALLY INSIDER
Learn the benefits of herbs and how to create a herbal compress on THE BARAI's Healing with Herbs Programme. Then relax and experience the results with a 90-minute signature Thai Herbal Compress treatment.

The Spa Apsara at The Sothea, National Road, Khum Svay Dangkhum, Siem Reap, Cambodia
Tel: +855 63 966 788 Fax: +855 63 966 789 Email: spa@thesothea.com Web: www.thesothea.com

Siem Reap | Cambodia

The Sothea

In Khmer mythology, the Apsaras are heavenly deities of beauty and grace – fitting inspirations for the spa at Siem Reap's newest luxury boutique resort, The Sothea. Built by a local businessman in honour of his wife, it is a tribute to femininity in both design and service values. Flowing waterways (water in Khmer mythology represents the female) circulate around flowering bushes, pink sandstone buildings and a striking gold-flecked, slate-tiled pool. In the spa, a mother-daughter programme with treatments made especially for teens and children offers a unique departure from the usual spa experience. Products are natural and organically based (either made exclusively for The Sothea or by Kerstin Florian USA) and therapies incorporate traditional Khmer healing techniques. There are three private treatment rooms with Jacuzzi and rain shower, two rooms for traditional massage, steam rooms, saunas and an Angkor-inspired courtyard for Yoga and meditation (also the setting for group 'spa afternoons' of healthy cuisine and light treatments). Personal butlers dedicated to each of the 39 suites will arrange guest itineraries from private in-suite Yoga sessions to relaxing post-party pampering – the spa stays open until 2am every night.

QUINTESSENTIALLY INSIDER
Experience the deep resonance of Angkor's ancient ruins by participating in a Yoga class within the archaeological site itself. Spa Apsara is the only spa in the area to offer this opportunity.

The Datai

Kedah Darul Aman | Malaysia

Beautifully integrated into the mystical Langkawi rainforest, the Spa at The Datai – one of the most desirable hotel destinations in Malaysia – promises the weary urbanite an idyllic return to nature. From film star to financier, this is the place to relax, rejuvenate and revitalise far away from the city hum. Inspired by the spirit and traditions of Bali, expert hands perform a comprehensive range of treatments in four enchanting spa pavilions. Hidden within the centuries-old virgin forest, the open-sided pavilions are connected by footpaths that wind between the trees to a private and inviting white sand beach below. Clean-lined and contemporary rooms, suites and villas also meander down the hillside. Each one is built in a traditional Malay style with warm woods and natural stone and each boasts a private veranda with spectacular views. There are two swimming pools, a range of watersports facilities, tennis courts, a gym and an 18-hole golf course cleverly landscaped to blend with the beauty of the rainforest; even the most active guests will not want of things to do.

QUINTESSENTIALLY INSIDER
If you're staying without kids don your designer sunglasses and head for the architecturally stunning Upper Pool restricted to over-16s only.

The Spa at The Datai, The Datai Langkawi, Jalan Teluk Datai, Langkawi, Kedah Darul Aman, Malaysia
Tel: +604 959 2500 Fax: +604 959 2600 Email: spamgr@thedatai.com.my Web: www.ghmhotels.com

Terengganu | Malaysia

Spa Village Tanjong Jara

In a secluded forest clearing on the east coast of Peninsular Malaysia, Tanjong Jara Resort and its spa is spread across a lush expanse of verdant greenery overlooking the golden sands and turquoise waters of the South China Sea. Designed to reflect the elegance and grandeur of 17th century Malay palaces in both architecture and way of life, Spa Village Tanjong Jara is the only luxury spa in the world to focus solely on traditional Malay healing arts. Every treatment begins with a Mandi Bunga (floral bath) traditionally practiced in Malay weddings to rid the body of negative energies and leave couples radiant and glowing. The practices, handed down from generation to generation, are believed to originate from Malay, Arab, Indian and Chinese influences during the days of the Malacca Sultanate. The philosophy of the resort is the Malay concept of *sucimurni,* which roughly translates as 'wellness through purity of mind, body and spirit'. All areas of the resort from its treatment menu to its relaxed, serene atmosphere are anchored in this philosophy – even the cookery classes.

QUINTESSENTIALLY INSIDER
Ask for Pak Yahya, a local midwife whose traditional healing techniques have been proved worthy of both local and international acclaim.

Spa Village Tanjong Jara, Tanjong Jara Resort, Batu 8, Off Jalan Dungun, Dungun, Terengganu, Malaysia
Tel: +603 2783 1000 Fax: + 603 2148 7397 Email: travelcentre@ytlhotels.com.my Web: www.spavillage.com

Damai, Grand Hyatt Singapore, 10 Scotts Road, Singapore
Tel: +65 6738 1234 Fax: +65 6732 1696 Email: damai.sg@hyatt.com Web: www.singapore.grand.hyatt.com

Grand Hyatt Singapore

Following a multi-million dollar refurbishment, Damai, the new spa at Grand Hyatt Singapore, is a destination in itself. Smack in the middle of Singapore's central business district, 11 sleek treatment rooms – sanctuaries of soothing colour tones and soft mood lighting – are surrounded by tropical gardens. Each treatment room, designed by award-winning Japanese design agency Super Potato, features locally sourced elements such as yellow balau timber, earthen walls, teak floors, and mannari stones as well as its own water feature and outdoor garden to give guests a feeling of direct contact with nature. Inspired by the Singaporean lifestyle, the Damai's impressive menu brings together healing philosophies, techniques, and traditions of Chinese, Malay, Indian, and European cultures as practiced in Singapore. Products made using raw natural ingredients are combined with customised paraben and preservative free products from New York spa visionary June Jacobs. In addition, there are steam and sauna rooms (the latter with built in televisions), Jacuzzi and a well-equipped fitness centre offering personal training, fitness classes, Pilates, Yoga and nutritional advice.

QUINTESSENTIALLY INSIDER
Take a tip from the likes of Madonna, Justin Timberlake and Eva Longoria and try an Intraceuticals Infusion®. Exclusively at Damai, the 60-minute pain-free, non-invasive skin treatment is a Hollywood must-have.

Spa Alila, Alila Villas Uluwatu, Jl Belimbing Sari, Banjar Tambiyak, Desa Pecatu, Bali, Indonesia
Tel: +62 361 848 2166 Fax: +62 361 848 2188 Email: uluwatu@alilahotels.com Web: www.alilahotels.com/uluwatu

Bali | Indonesia

Spa Alila

Spa Alila at Alila Villas Uluwatu is perched on a plateau 100metres above the Indian Ocean on Bali's south coast. Its contemporary clean-lined design, courtesy of award-winning architect firm WOHA, perfectly complements the dramatic cliff top surroundings. Walkways and bridges connect relaxation pavilions and pools with spacious accommodation at Alila Villas Uluwatu. A gentle sea breeze circulates throughout the open-plan design and Balinese-style accents of dark wood, carved stone and rattan furniture celebrate the island's culture. The resort also boasts impressive eco-credentials (involving water and energy conservation) ensuring guests here can unwind with a clear conscience. The spa boasts a mineral pool and five individual treatment villas. Four of which may be booked in their entirety and include herbal steam showers, bathtubs, treatment beds and relaxing day beds – perfect for couples wishing to enjoy a combination of pampering and privacy. Treatments span a wide range of therapeutic massages, facials and body scrubs using Spa Alila's natural handmade products. Exercise, Yoga and meditation classes are on offer along with a variety of healthy eating options and recommendations for improved wellbeing.

QUINTESSENTIALLY INSIDER
On request spa therapists can perform treatments in the privacy of your own villa. Ask for yours under a star-studded sky by the private pool and listen to the waves crashing below – Spa Alila's four-handed *Shirodhara* massage comes highly recommended.

COMO Shambhala Estate, Ubud, Bali, Indonesia
Tel: +62 361 978 888 Fax: +62 361 978 889 Email: info@cse.comoshambhala.bz Web: www.cse.como.bz

Bali | Indonesia

COMO Shambhala Estate

COMO Shambhala Estate is an exceptional residential wellness retreat in the heart of rural Bali. It is far more than a pampering spa, providing a total, 360-degree experience designed to rejuvenate and repair mind, body and spirit. This is achieved through specialist staff – including a resident nutritionist, Ayurvedic doctor, Yoga and Pilates instructors – as well as carefully designed wellness programmes including Detox, Ayurveda, Anti-Ageing Rejuvenation, Get Fit and Stress Management. Set amidst verdant jungle scenery on the banks of the winding Ayung river, accommodation and facilities which do not skimp on privacy, luxury or personal space. Ojas, which forms the heart of the property, comprises nine treatment rooms (including three for couples). An open air Vitality Pool boasts views over lush greenery to Mount Batu Karu in the distance. There is an outdoor Jungle Gym, an open-sided Yoga pavilion, Pilates studio, a rock climbing wall and a riverside treatment area where specialists perform a wide range of Asian-inspired therapies. Water from The Source, a sacred spring within the Estate's grounds and long revered by locals for its healing, mineral-rich properties, is used for water-based therapies. But, most of all, it is the deep-set spirituality of the place that makes The Estate unique – this and the exceptional villa-style accommodation.

QUINTESSENTIALLY INSIDER
For an opportunity to study Yoga with the world's best (including American Rodney Yee) check out the property's website detailing news of The Estate's regular Retreats with Visiting Masters.

75

The Spa, Bulgari Hotels and Resorts, Jalan Goa Lempeh, Banjar Dinas Kangin, Uluwatu, Bali, Indonesia
Tel: +62 361 847 1000 Fax: +62 361 847 1111 Email: bali.reservations@bulgarihotels.com Web: www.bulgarihotels.com

Bali | Indonesia

Following the success of its first hotel in Milan, Bulgari has chosen Bali's far southwestern tip for its place in the sun; an Asian outpost where cool contemporary Italian design meets Balinese culture. Sitting atop a 160 metre high cliff, not far from the sacred temple at Uluwatu, the resort's funicular transports guests to the talc-white beaches below. A magnificent spa complex plus 59 villas, two restaurants and a large pool gaze out over an expanse of glittering Indian Ocean. Guests are welcomed into the spa hospitality lounge via an original, intricately carved *Joglo* (18th century house) transported from the Javanese city of Kudus. Beyond this, peaceful gardens and a tranquil pond surround eight treatment rooms. There is a relaxation lounge with a plunge pool, a Yoga pavilion and a beauty salon. The combination of Balinese, Asian and European therapies include Hot Stone Massage, Ayurvedic rituals and an unforgettable Double Bulgari Royal Lulur Bath.

QUINTESSENTIALLY INSIDER
In-villa massages are available and best enjoyed after a butler-drawn bath – the bathtubs at Bulgari Bali have been described as 'altars to purity', request yours infused with ESPA mineral bath salts and laced with fresh flower petals.

Kayumanis Ubud, Sayan Village, Ubud, Bali, Indonesia
Tel: +62 361 705 777 Fax: +62 361 705 101 Email: spa@kayumanis.com Web: www.kayumanis.com

Bali | Indonesia

Kayumanis Ubud

Unveiled last year, the new spa at Kayumanis Ubud is the jewel in this visionary hospitality group's wellness crown. Secluded within its own woodland sanctuary, it is separated from the guest villas by the Lauh River and only accessible via a private footbridge. The Kayumanis group encompasses five properties on the island of Bali, each one designed to harmonise with its immediate location and each with its own signature spa venue. At Ubud, 23 one-, two- or three-bed traditional Balinese villas are tastefully themed with a choice of Balinese, Javanese, Oriental, Palembang, Primitive or Modern interiors. All enjoy absolute privacy, private pools and ever-ready butler service. On the opposite river bank the spa comprises thatched treatment pavilions that seamlessly blend into the trees; an open deck provides a platform for Yoga, meditation and inner contemplation. Rejuvenating treatments, created to smooth away the effects of a busy modern lifestyle, combine wisdoms from across Asia and include a selection of indulgent bath rituals. In a conscious effort to maintain wholesome and sustainable traditions, products are homemade from indigenous herbs, spices, flowers, fruit and plant extracts known to replenish and nurture the skin.

QUINTESSENTIALLY INSIDER
Each Kayumanis Spa has its own signature treatment reflecting the character of its surroundings. At Kayumanis Ubud experience Yoga and a refreshing river walk followed by a pampering full body scrub, wrap and hot volcanic stone massage.

Alila Villas Soori, Banjar Dukuh, Desa Kelating, Kerambitan, Tabanan, Bali, Indonesia
Tel: +65 6735 8300 Email: soori@alilahotels.com Web: www.alilahotels.com/soori

Bali | Indonesia

Alila Villas Soori

Alila Hotels and Resorts have chosen a gentle slope between verdant rice terraces and a beautiful black-sand beach on Bali's southwest coast for their forth property on the island – due to open in November this year. Expect Alila's trademark contemporary Asian design and relaxed ambiance in 38 pool villas plus nine three-bedroom residential villas all perfectly positioned to enjoy panoramic ocean views and breezes. Spa Alila will be set beneath a reflection pond, creating a secluded sanctuary with an aqua ceiling filling the spa with soothing watery light. Five deluxe spa rooms will be available for couples requiring more privacy; each one fully equipped with herbal steam showers, bathtubs, treatment beds and day beds as well private entrances. Spa Alila fervently believes in all things natural; products are handmade using fresh locally sourced ingredients and intuitive therapists will deliver unique spa treatments derived from ancient Asian healing techniques. Exercise, Yoga and meditation will feature highly, as will correct nutrition. Therapists trained in anatomy, physiology and massage will offer consultations and self-care recommendations to help guests maintain personal wellbeing.

QUINTESSENTIALLY INSIDER
Don't miss the opportunity to ride horses on the black sands of Kelating Beach. The nearby Royal Stable offers various horseback programmes including three-hour accompanied tours that take in villages, rivers, rice fields and the beaches.

Water's Edge, Park Hyatt Shanghai, 100 Century Avenue, Pudong New Area, Shanghai, China
Tel: +86 216 888 9482 Email: shanghai.Park@hyatt.com Web: www.parkhyattshanghai.com

Shanghai | China

Water's Edge

Last year's hottest new opening, the Park Hyatt Shanghai on the 79th to the 93rd floor of Shanghai's World Financial Centre is the highest hotel in the world (it stole the title from its sister hotel, Grand Hyatt Shanghai, across the street). High above the city on the vertiginous 85th floor the Water's Edge spa has sweeping views of the Pudong skyline. Inspired by Chinese tradition and wisdom, the spa's name is derived from the Chinese place of honour – always at the water's edge. Chinese health and wellbeing practices are incorporated into the menu under the 'Tradition' category designed to restore balance to body and mind. The *Tui Na* massage, for example, literally translates as 'press and rub' and combines acupressure with reflexology, it is particularly recommended for jet-lagged guests. The spa also offers 'Escape' treatments for deep relaxation and 'Flow' treatments to energise and free the spirit. Treatments are followed by Chinese or fruit tea, which may be sipped on a Dedon day bed by the elegant art-deco-styled infinity-edge pool. Facilities also include a wellness studio, steam room, sauna and whirlpool.

QUINTESSENTIALLY INSIDER
Start the day Chinese style with Tai Chi in the spa's sky-high courtyard. Classes with the Tai Chi master take place every morning from 8:00 'till 9:00.

The Peninsula Hong Kong

Hong Kong | China

The Peninsula Spa by ESPA occupies the seventh and ninth floors of Hong Kong's legendary Peninsula hotel, it is a chic idyll in the heart of a fast-paced city. In the 1920s the hotel represented a much yearned for respite for weary voyagers just off the boats. Today 'the finest hotel east of Suez', still hailed as one of the best in the world, maintains a similar – although more sophisticated – service for today's well-heeled travellers. Treatment rooms, relaxation areas and saunas afford stunning views across Victoria Harbour. The Asian Tea Lounge features a crystal water wall with optic lights where guests can relax and sample The Peninsula's own organic blend of tea. There are crystal steam rooms plus tropical and arctic mist experience showers that use aromatherapy and colour therapy to cool and tone the skin. But the *pièce de résistance* is the magnificent Roman-style swimming pool on the eighth floor with huge carved columns and superb views of the Hong Kong skyline through a retractable glass wall.

QUINTESSENTIALLY INSIDER
Sample one of the eight signature treatments. Created exclusively for The Peninsula by ESPA, these unique treatments fuse Oriental and Ayurvedic philosophies for an entirely new holistic experience.

The Peninsula Spa by ESPA, 7/F The Peninsula Hong Kong, Salisbury Road, Kowloon, Hong Kong, China
Tel: +85 22 315 3322 Fax: +85 22 315 3325 Email: spaphk@peninsula.com Web: www.peninsula.com

Victoria | Australia

Aurora Spa Retreat

Minutes from the beach in the edgy and bohemian suburb of St Kilda, Aurora is Melbourne's leading holistic day spa (endorsed by Sting, no less). The spa is spread over two levels of the award-winning Prince Hotel which itself provides a great base for those embarking on Aurora's customised retreat programmes. Sleek architecture creates a sensuous reflective space where light is controlled through textured glass panels. There are 22 treatment areas including one with a custom-made Swiss shower overlooking the bay. Purpose built facilities include a water therapies suite with single and double treatment steam rooms, geisha spa and Vichy shower. The menu combines everything from 19th century European water therapies to Native American rituals and indigenous Australian healing wisdoms. But Aurora's core philosophy lies in the changing of the seasons and a belief that optimum health, wellness and happiness can be best achieved when the body is in harmony with the rhythm of nature. This notion underlies all treatments with the inclusion of colour therapy, rituals and crystals aligned with each season.

QUINTESSENTIALLY INSIDER
Ask for the award-winning Kitya Karnu Signature Treatment - a desert salt body exfoliation in a private steam room incorporating a mini facial and scalp massage.

Aurora Spa Retreat, 2 Acland Street, St Kilda, Victoria, Australia
Tel: +61 395 361 130 Fax: +61 395 253 729 Email: info@aurorasparetreat.com Web: www.aurorasparetreat.com

Spa Hayman, Hayman, Great Barrier Reef, Australia
Tel: +61 749 401 234 Fax: +61 749 401 858 Email: reservations@hayman.com.au Web: www.hayman.com.au

Hayman | Australia

Spa Hayman

Hayman, Australia's celebrated private island retreat surrounded by the breathtaking Great Barrier Reef, offers a genuine island experience of remoteness and natural beauty whilst pampering guests with exceptional luxury. Spa Hayman is consistently acknowledged as being one of the best in Australia. An array of magnificent treatments and a selection of personally tailored health and spa programmes can be delivered indoors or outdoors enabling guests to appreciate the island's colourful flora and exotic wildlife. The spa features 13 individual treatment rooms, a hydrotherapy area, Vichy shower, sauna and steam rooms, two relaxation lounges and a small boutique selling natural source Pevonia Botanica products used in the spa. Outdoor massage pavilions are nestled in lush gardens by tranquil waters and face out over the white sand and bright blue coral sea towards the neighbouring Whitsunday Islands. The wonderful reef location provides a host of opportunities to explore above and below water, while the resort itself offers activities including tennis, squash, golf putting and driving and fitness facilities. Alternatively guests may simply hide away in the superbly appointed rooms, suites, penthouse or villa either on the beachfront, overlooking a tranquil lagoon, tucked within peaceful gardens or with direct access and views of the famous Hayman Pool.

QUINTESSENTIALLY INSIDER
Enjoy an in-water Ocean Massage, a Hayman Signature Experience, surrounded by gentle tides and tropical fish in the warm Whitsunday sun.

The Americas

It is not difficult to see why the beautiful, fertile lands of the Americas have been colonised by people from every corner of the globe. The continent has an abundance of natural resources and is home many spectacular landscapes. The Americas are a popular destination with adventure-seekers wishing to explore 'off the beaten track', as well as with holiday-makers looking for something a little more civilised, with all the comforts of home.

The indigenous people of America worshipped nature and all her bounties. They lived at one with the land, taking from it only what they needed to survive, whilst respecting the delicate balance of the natural world. Traditional Native American therapies are still used in spas to this day, many of them unchanged for hundreds of years.

Hot stone therapy is thought to have originated in the Central Americas. Basalt stones, worn smooth over the years by the rivers, were heated over fires and used to relieve muscle pain. The Native people believed that the stones absorbed the spirit of nature and had mystical powers. Hot stone massage has now become popular all over the world, with the stones being placed over the body on energy points before being incorporated into the massage itself. Hot stone massage is simply heavenly; a wonderful combination of hands-on therapy complemented by the sensation of smooth, heavy stones, warmed to perfection.

Aloe vera, although thought to have originated in Africa, has been found to have been evident in the Americas for thousands of years. The gel inside the leaves was applied to the skin to treat burns, insect bites and even open cuts. The Aloe plant has fantastic healing properties, and its high water content makes it a great treatment for dehydrated skin. Perhaps America's most famous export is the cocoa bean. Regarded by the Aztecs as divine – they called it 'the food of the Gods' – it was so valuable that it was used as currency. Cocoa, and the chocolate made from it, has high levels of magnesium, a mineral needed for elastin, as well as many important antioxidants. It has been shown to release endorphins and spas have taken notice of this to create rich, dreamy face packs, body masks and massage oils, all incorporating this super-indulgent ingredient.

The beautiful islands of the Caribbean have a long-standing reputation as being perfect luxury holiday destinations. Their incredible diversity, both in landscape and culture, has attracted visitors from all over the world for hundreds of years. The seven thousand-strong island chain boasts year round sunshine, warm turquoise seas and miles of picturesque beaches and rainforest, together with its famous laid-back atmosphere.

A typical Caribbean spa treatment is a wonderful mix of therapies and ingredients from every corner of the globe. Influences from Asia, Europe and Africa are combined with local plants and flowers giving classic, age-old therapies. The highly prized oil extracted from the Frangipani flower is one of the most sought-after ingredients in skin care. Known as 'the flower of the Gods' the oil has been used in preparations for centuries to soothe, relax and moisturise the skin.

The unmistakeably sensual fragrance of the flower also makes it a popular ingredient for bath milks, body oils and perfumes.

Coconut oil is another iconic spa ingredient of the Caribbean and the Tropics. The luxurious oil has been used in traditional preparations to condition dry and brittle hair, giving it incredible shine. Coconut extract is known to have regenerating properties, making it a fantastic treatment for sunburn and dry skin.

We have searched the Americas and Caribbean to offer you an outstanding collection of spa resorts in the most beautiful of locations. Whether you desire a massage in tropical surrounding, or some time out from the hustle and bustle of the city, you should find your perfect spa break here.

Shibui Spa at the Greenwich Hotel, 377 Greenwich Street, New York, USA
Tel: +1 646 203 0045 Fax: +1 212 9418 6000 Email: shibui@thegreenwichhotle.com Web: www.thegreenwichhotel.com

New York | USA

Shibui Spa

Shibui Spa located in Robert De Niro's new Greenwich Hotel in trendy TriBeCa, is like no other in New York. Constructed by Japanese craftsmen using materials mainly imported from Japan, it offers a true escape from the frenetic city outside. The ambiance is that of a Japanese tea-house with a stunning azure swimming pool and lounge area lit by Japanese lanterns and dominated by the roof of a 250 year old wood and bamboo farmhouse. A holistic approach to relaxation and rejuvenation employs healing rituals from various eastern cultures and an upscale range of organic, botanical and natural products – some of which are handcrafted specifically for the spa. There are five treatment rooms with traditional plaster-and-straw walls, a shiatsu room, a private Japanese bathing room with a tatami mat floor and a wet room for wraps and scrubs. Even the huge fitness room is designed with serenity in mind; old hemlock floors and subtle lighting is coupled with the most state-of-the art equipment.

QUINTESSENTIALLY INSIDER

Try the 80-minute Lotus Root Remedy; a warm soothing preparation of Lotus essences, organic oils and herbal waxes rich in skin protective properties. It is slowly massaged onto your entire body before setting into a warm cocooning mask. The experience finishes with a Jasmine and Gardenia body scrub.

The Spa at Mandarin Oriental New York, 80 Columbus Circle at 60th Street, New York, USA
Tel: +1 212 805 8880 Fax: +1 212 805 8886 Email: monyc-spa@mohg.com Web: mandarinoriental.com/newyork

New York | USA

Mandarin Oriental New York

High above the hustle and bustle of Manhattan's city streets on the 35th floor of the Time Warner Centre at Columbus Circle, The Spa at Mandarin Oriental, New York is a calm oasis of pure, understated luxury (voted by readers of *Condé Nast Traveller* as one of the America's top spas in 2009). The décor mixes light wood and gold leaf; the atmosphere is tranquil and relaxing. Guests may spend their time in the amethyst crystal steam rooms or be gently massaged by hydrotherapy jets in the vitality pools. Signature teas, fruit smoothies and healthy *hors d'oeuvres* are served prior to treatments in the Oriental Tea Lounge – or afterwards in the relaxation rooms. Wellness rituals derived from the ancient traditions of China, Bali and Thailand are combined with modern western techniques. The Thai Yoga Massage is performed in its own custom-designed room and the Mandarin Oriental's new signature spa therapies provide guests with tailored treatments based on the principals of traditional Chinese medicine and aromatherapy.

QUINTESSENTIALLY INSIDER
In-the-know Manhattanites book the exquisite 60 metre sq VIP Spa Suite for three hours of complete bliss. Two guests can enjoy side-by-side treatments, use the private steam room and sauna, enjoy stunning views from the raised soaking tub or relax in front of a roaring fire.

Yelo Wellness, 315 West 57 street, New York, USA
Tel: +1 212 245 8235 Email: treats@yelonyc.com Web: www.yelonyc.com

New York | USA

Yelo Wellness

In the city that never sleeps Yelo is a unique wellness concept for stressed out New Yorkers which extols the benefits of the power nap (or YeloNap® as it has been re-branded here). Creator Nicolas Ronco was a travelling businessman on the verge of burnout when he discovered the rewards reflexology and a daytime sleep. Yelo does not call itself a spa because water is not used in the treatments offered. But the end result is the same: relaxation and rejuvenation in very large helpings. A nap of between 20 and 40 minutes has been medically proven to increase alertness and productivity. Treatments at Yelo take place in private honeycomb-shaped cocoons (YeloCabs®) that can be customised in terms of music, lighting and scent. Within each YeloCab® is a YeloChair® designed to position the legs above the heart. This slows the pulse and produces a feeling of weightlessness encouraging the body to settle quickly into a natural state of deep relaxation. A standard treatment consists of a calming half-hour reflexology session, which may include pressure to reflex points on the hands and ears as well as to the feet, followed by a half-hour nap – simple but incredibly effective.

QUINTESSENTIALLY INSIDER
Yelo is not just for New York's frazzled workforce, Yelo's Travelade treatment is specifically designed for International jet-setters. A 10-minute head, neck and shoulder massage followed by 30 minutes of reflexology and a 20-minute nap is a perfect antidote to jet lag.

Caudalíe Vinothérapie® Spa, The Plaza Hotel, Fifth Avenue at Central Park South, New York, USA
Tel: + 1 212 265 3182 Email: theplaza@fairmont.com Web: www.theplaza.com

The Plaza Hotel

Last October Mathilde and Bertrand Thomas, founders of Caudalíe, opened their first state-side spa on the fourth floor of New York's iconic Plaza Hotel overlooking Central Park. The couple from Bordeaux, who discovered the extraordinary anti-oxidant powers of grapes and grapevine polyphenols in 1993, already operate two award-winning spas in European vineyard settings (at Châteaux Smith Haut Lafitte vineyard in Bordeaux and the Frank Gehry designed Marqués de Riscal in Riojas) and another has recently opened at Le Etangs de Corot near Versailles. The spas offer exclusive wine-themed treatments such as the Crushed Cabernet Scrub, Fresh Grape Massage and a menu of world-famous Caudalíe facials. This new Caudalíe Vinothérapie® Spa brings the vineyard experience to the city and has already attracted an entitled clientele. Between soaking in a barrel bath infused with red vine and crushed grape extracts, and a session in the beautiful tiled hammam, guests may retreat to the French Paradox Wine Lounge. Here wine is served by resident sommelier Cliff Rames and decadent 'small plates' include a selection of French cheeses, smoked duck breast and foie gras.

QUINTESSENTIALLY INSIDER

Let your hands and feet also benefit from the restorative effects of grape extracts with the special Fresh Grape Manicure and Pedicure only available at The Plaza.

Mayflower Inn and Spa, 118 Woodbury Road, Washington, Connecticut, USA
Tel: +1 860 868 9466 Fax: +1 860 868 1497 Email: inn@mayflowerinn.com Web: www.mayflowerinn.com

Connecticut | USA

Mayflower Inn and Spa

Less than two hours from New York, the 19th century Mayflower Inn and Spa welcomes stressed out city types wanting to relax and luxuriate in its cosseting confines. Accommodating just 30 to 60 guests at any one time, the opulent New England inn features romantic rooms and suites with high canopy beds, mountains of pillows, gas fireplaces and deep soaking tubs. Nestled at the heart of the 56-acre estate, Spa House offers Mayflower guests a seriously spoiling spa facility. There are eight treatment rooms, a thermal sanctuary, scented steam rooms, a heated indoor pool and various Yoga, Pilates and exercise studios. Therapists, fitness staff and dedicated spa advisors ensure guests receive the appropriate spa experience. Weekenders may dip in and out, indulging in the odd pampering moment and enjoying the spa's sun-drenched garden room. But the real focus here is the thoroughly personalised five-night Destination Spa Programme. Adopting a holistic approach to wellness these programmes combine, relaxing and cleansing therapies with good nutrition, bodywork and education – and it doesn't end when you check out, spa staff will stay in contact to make sure you keep up the good work.

QUINTESSENTIALLY INSIDER
Check out the website for the spa's calendar of speciality weeks including Yoga retreats, sleep therapy and inspired self-discovery workshops.

ONE SPA at Shutters on the Beach, 1 Pico Blvd, Santa Monica, California, USA
Tel: +1 310 587 1712 Web: www.shuttersonthebeach.com

California | USA

Shutters on the Beach

Known for its inspirational interiors, Shutters on the Beach at Santa Monica Bay, has recently been reinvented by LA-based interior designer Micheal Smith, renowned for his dramatic residential makeovers on both coasts (and newly appointed designer at the Obama White House). He has also given his attention to the hotel's new Spa – a first for Smith. Inspired by the yachting scene of the 1930s, ONE SPA interiors are sleek and clean with portholes in the seven treatment rooms and a charming shell-lined relaxation room. Two wet treatment rooms also have Shutter's exclusive rain showers. The extensive spa menu features treatments from skin-care specialist Ole Henriksen, whose celebrity client list includes Oscar winning ladies Charlize Theron and Renee Zellweger. His principles of simplicity, renewal, stimulation, hydration and pampering offer therapeutic benefits for both skin and soul. There is a chic pool for seeing and being seen, a fitness studio and Yoga regularly takes place on the beach. Yoga is one of the most popular health regimes in California and classes are free for guests as well as ONE SPA's fashionable local day members.

QUINTESSENTIALLY INSIDER
If you like Henriksen's all-natural, botanical-infused and cruelty-free products you can buy them at the spa or pick them up from the website, www.shuttersbeachstyle.com, which also features a range of products to help you style your home Shutters way.

Post Ranch Inn, Highway 1, Big Sur, California, USA
Tel: +1 800 527 2200 Fax: +1 831 667 2512 Email: reservations@postranchinn.com Web: www.postranchinn.com

California | USA

Post Ranch Inn

Post Ranch Inn has long been a regular presence on lists of top luxury hotels, best spas and most-romantic getaways. It's a favourite of California's A-list crowd and the setting is truly spectacular - 350 metres above the crashing surf on Big Sur's wild and beautiful coastline. A string of architecturally stunning suites, rooms and houses built in slate, glass, wood and rusting metal to blend with the landscape, cling to both sides of a winding path. Within the totally private 100-acre compound, two cliff-top soaking pools offer awe-inspiring ocean views: the Jade Pool decorated with jade stones, hand-harvested from nearby rocky coves and the smooth stainless steel Meditation Pool. There is also a large swimming pool located in a sunny meadow. Towering redwoods frame spa treatment rooms with magnificent views of the granite peaks (including the exclusive Spa Suite with wood-burning fireplace, hydrotherapy bathtub and outdoor deck). A myriad of services harmonise body and soul combining massages, body treatments and facials (using certified organic products) with shaman sessions, sound therapy, Yoga and guided hikes. Post Ranch Inn is also a pioneer of green initiatives with one of the largest solar power systems of any resort in America, making this sanctuary a true meeting of nature and nurture.

QUINTESSENTIALLY INSIDER
Join the on-site astronomer for a spot of late evening star gazing. Far from the city, Big Sur's night sky is a pristine marvel of starry clarity.

Mii amo

Nestled within a sacred canyon at the heart of Arizona's 'Red Rock County', Mii amo is a destination spa with a Native American influence. Part of the exclusive Enchantment Resort, it is also a separate entity with its own accommodation and restaurant. There are 20 treatment rooms, many with dramatic canyon views, plus five outdoor treatment areas shaded by *wikiup*-inspired wooden trellises. The heart and soul of Mii amo is the Crystal Grotto, a reflection and meditation space with a circular aperture directed at the sun on the summer solstice. The name Mii amo is taken from the Yuman Indian word meaning Himalayas 'to continue one's path', and many guests here seek transformation on programmes known as a Journeys. Treatments tend towards the spiritual with a range of metaphysical therapies and consultations – although more traditional massage, Ayurveda, facials and hydrotherapy are also featured. Exercise takes the form of Yoga with two classes a day; also dance including Spirit Dance (a blend of sounds, movements, rhythms and breathing techniques), as well as other, more typical fitness options.

QUINTESSENTIALLY INSIDER
Pack light, most guests remain in their robe all day. But remember your swimsuit – there are two outdoor pools and you shouldn't miss a session in the Whirlpool under the Sedona night sky.

Mii amo, 525 Boynton Canyon Road, Sedona, Arizona, USA
Tel: +1 888 749 2137 or +1 928 203 8500 Email: info@miiamo.com Web: www.miiamo.com

Arizona | USA

Canyon Ranch

Husband and wife team Mel and Enid Zuckerman opened Canyon Ranch in 1979 after the simple realisation that healthy living was the key to a happy life. Years and many accolades later, Canyon Ranch still inspires the guests who flock here and it's still considered one of America's premier health spas. The property occupies a 200-acre site in the sunny Sonoran Desert, an oasis of health and vitality with an unhurried, holiday atmosphere. Guests can embark on a fitness programme, enjoy indulgent body and beauty treatments, explore spiritual pathways, take healthy cooking classes or hike in canyons and pine-topped mountains. There is an Aquatic Centre with cross-training and therapeutic pools plus individual pools for Watsu® (in water massage) and a Golf Performance Centre with PGA pros and the latest equipment. A multitude of highly qualified experts – physicians, nutritionists, life management experts, movement therapists, exercise physiologists and more – all work together to achieve what's right for the individual, whether that's a week of blissful pampering or a life-enhancing transformation.

QUINTESSENTIALLY INSIDER
Don't miss the opportunity to have a Biophysical 250® – a blood assessment that provides the single most comprehensive health evaluation available.

Canyon Ranch, 8600 E. Rockcliff Rd, Tucson, Arizona, USA
Tel: +1 800 742 9000 Fax: +1 520 239 8535 Email: info@canyonranch.com Web: www.canyonranch.com

Amanyara, Providenciales, Turks and Caicos Islands
Tel: +1 649 941 8133 Email: amanyara@amanresorts.com Web: www.amanresorts.com/amanyara

Amanyara

Amanyara, Amanresorts only Caribbean outpost, has recently debuted the Serenity Villa, a 1,200 metre sq wellness facility. Set on the rugged northwest point of the main island of Providenciales, beside a vast sweep of untouched beach, Aman's simple Asian-inspired architecture and barefoot chic blends seamlessly with the landscape. Guests are welcomed into The Serenity Villa via a large reception pavilion and comfortable lounge where herbal teas and health drinks are served. Four large treatment pavilions surround a 10 meter pool lined with *chaises longues* (that's in addition to the resorts main infinity-edge pool fashioned from dramatic black lava). Signature massages and luxurious body treatments incorporate Amanresorts' custom-blended line of body products using natural and locally-sourced ingredients. A Master in Residence programme is designed to guide guests through the latest holistic healing practices. From Emotional Freedom Techniques (EFT) to the work of Byron Katie or Integrative Bodywork, guests are led on a personal quest to achieve dynamic integration of mind, body and spirit. Individual or group Yoga, Pilates and Reformer classes are also available in a private studio or an outside *sala* that practically floats on a tranquil pond.

QUINTESSENTIALLY INSIDER
Request one of the two treatment rooms with outdoor showers and soaking tubs set within a small garden. Relax in a warm bath outdoors beneath a radiantly sunny sky or, even better, as sunset streaks across the horizon.

Anani Spa, Grace Bay Club, Providenciales, Turks and Caicos Islands
Tel: +1 649 946 5050 Fax: +1 649 946 5758 Email: info@gracebayclub.com Web: www.gracebayclub.com

Anani Spa

The Grace Bay Club opened in 1992 as Providenciale's first luxury hotel – a charming Spanish-style building comprising just 21 rooms. But thanks to new ownership and a whopping cash injection of $140 million, the Caribbean resort has undergone an impressive transformation. Designed in the spirit of a Mediterranean seaside village, it now features 38 family villas and a brand new privately owned beachfront estate in addition to the original hotel – now completely renovated and up-dated. There is also a new Infiniti Bar – the Caribbean's longest bar – which stretches almost 30 metres across the Grace Bay Club to the shores of Grace Bay Beach. In 2005 the Anani Spa, moved out of its tented lodgings on the beach and into its own air-conditioned digs with six treatment rooms, a manicure/pedicure room, *alfresco* showers, steam rooms and a relaxation room. This year, due to popular demand the spa has re-introduced two permanent luxury spa tents back down on the sugar-white sand where nostalgic guests can enjoy a multitude of Euro-Asian spa treatments just feet from the Grace Bay shore. Spread out over 11 acres with 335metres of private beachfront the resort still affords plenty of elbowroom, personal concierges cater to every whim and Grace Bay Club remains one of the most desirable destinations in the Turks and Caicos.

QUINTESSENTIALLY INSIDER
Make sure you book the spa tents before you get to the resort – they are hugely popular particularly among romance-seeking couples.

Rendezvous Bay | Anguilla

CuisinArt Resort & Spa

Anguilla's über-luxury award-winning CuisinArt Resort & Spa unveiled its newly expanded Venus Spa last year. Set back from the powder white beach of Rendezvous Bay and separate from the main hotel, the facility is now three times its original size. Sixteen state-of-the-art treatment rooms including wet rooms, lavish massage and facial rooms, VIP and couples suites with outdoor showers, have all been designed with the same Greek-island influence as seen throughout the resort. Treatments are also inspired by the Mediterranean with many using sea, salt and seaweed as ingredients, plus there's a new custom-designed Healing Waters Aquatherapy Pool – the first of its kind in the Caribbean. Massages include everything from Reiki and deep-tissue to a Caribbean hot stone therapy. An exotic range of wraps, scrubs and facials use fresh organic ingredients sourced daily from CuisinArt's unique Hydroponic Farm – which also supplies the resort's restaurants. There is an exclusive Men's Club Room, beautifully designed hammams, a second floor relaxation room with extraordinary sea views and possibly one of the most glamorous manicure and pedicure areas in the world.

QUINTESSENTIALLY INSIDER
CuisinArt Resort & Spa takes its food seriously – don't miss the exclusive Chef's Table Dining Experience with wine pairing from the resort's cellar. Also the Lobster and Caribbean nights – they're the best on the island.

113

The Spa, Hotel Saint-Barth Isle de France, Baie des Flamands, Saint Barthelemy, French West Indies
Tel: +59 059 027 5860 Email: spa@isle-de-france.com Web: www.isle-de-france.com

Flamands | Saint Barthelemy

The Spa at Hotel Saint-Barth Isle de France

The Spa at Hotel Saint-Barth Isle de France is the only Molton Brown spa outside Europe. Anchored on one of St. Barts' most beautiful beaches with 37 huge luxuriously appointed rooms, suites and villas all with four-poster beds, French fabrics and fine art, there are many good reasons to stay at this intimate resort. The Molton Brown protocol brings together a selection of massage and therapies from around the world. Thai massage, Indian head massage, hot stones massage and Swedish massage are all on the menu as well as the opportunity to indulge in a traditional Turkish bath treatment with exfoliating black soap, steam and massage in the spa's hammam. The popular product range is rooted in the principals of aromatherapy, respectful of mind, body and the environment. There are five treatment rooms including one outside pavilion where individuals or couples can choose to be surrounded by tranquil tropical gardens and the relaxing sound of birdsong. Wellbeing classes, Yoga, Tai Chi, Pilates and acupuncture are also offered to help guests achieve absolute serenity.

QUINTESSENTIALLY INSIDER
Jump-start your stay with a Shiatsu Body Massage. A perfect antidote to replenish and reawaken the body's vital energies. The treatment will quickly get you into the Caribbean swing leaving you feeling refreshed, supple and uplifted.

St. James | Barbados

Coral Reef Club

The eagerly awaited spa at Barbados' Coral Reef Club opened late last year in a beautiful colonial-inspired building set within a tropical garden paradise. Its classic charm combined with its modern design aesthetic has already won the spa widespread acclaim. The family-owned hotel, quietly nestled in 12 acres of lush vegetation on the island's famed west coast, has enticed guests for over 50 years with its elegant colonial atmosphere, perfect white-sand beach, superb food and array of water sports. The new spa completes the picture. Exotic vegetation and water features continue throughout the spa accentuating the notion that interior and exterior are one. An outdoor pavilion for couples, a hydro-pool surrounded by shaded cabanas, an open-sided relaxation room and a manicure/pedicure room with striking views over the tree tops celebrate the island's natural beauty and tranquillity. In four multipurpose treatment rooms (each boasting its own private garden) guests may choose from a range of exotic signature body scrubs, wraps and massages using locally sourced plants and fruits or treatments using the niche but fabulous Natura Bissé products.

QUINTESSENTIALLY INSIDER
For the ultimate in luxury accommodation, book a Plantation Suite with a huge canopied or four-poster bed, private plunge pool and stunning interior design.

Raffles Canouan

The fabulous Balinese-style Raffles Amrita Spa at Raffles Canouan comprises 11 thatched-roof double treatment suites with private ocean-view decks, Jacuzzis and day beds. Nine are scattered across a hillside, reached via an open-air, solar-powered elevator that rises up from the sea. The remaining two are accessible only by boat; set out over the water they feature glass floors and views of the coral reefs below. Morning Chi and mediation classes are offered from a beautiful tree palapa on the waters edge. The dazzling five star resort was designed by Italian architect Luigi Vietti, renowned for Porto Cervo, Hotel Pitizza and numerous other hotels and villas on the Emerald Coast of Sardinia. The 88 rooms and suites are set in a natural amphitheatre style overlooking the Caribbean Sea and the longest of the resort's three secluded white sand beaches. Each villa offers breathtaking views, some with private gardens, some with private pools. The resort also boasts the largest freshwater pool in the region, the Sugar Palm kid's club and a spectacular Jim Fazio-designed 18-hole championship Golf Course.

QUINTESSENTIALLY INSIDER
Even if Golf is not your thing, this course is worth a tour and every guest receives a complementary golf buggy, which is also useful for exploring the vast resort.

Raffles Canouan , St Vincent and The Grenadines, West Indies
Tel: +1 784 458 8000 Fax: +1 784 458 8885 Email: canouan@raffles.com Web: www.rafflescanouan.com

Mendoza | Argentina

Cavas Wine Lodge

There are several ways to immerse yourself in wine and at Cavas Wine Lodge, in Argentina's Mendoza wine region, guests are encouraged to try them all. Set in 35 acres of tranquil vineyards flanked by the year-round snowy peaks of the Andes, 14 deluxe guest vignettes (freestanding abode huts) sit amid the grapes. Each vignette is practically a mini spa; all have gigantic bathrooms with beautiful roll-top tubs, open-air showers and plunge pools on private mountain-facing terraces. Chill-out mattresses on the roofs make perfect relaxation platforms with 360-degree vineyard views. But the hotel's main spa is where true immersion takes place by way of a red wine bath – or rather a bath of hot bubbling water enriched with red wine extracts (wine and grape seed extracts are renowned for their anti-ageing properties). There's also the Malbec Scrub using crushed grape seeds from Cavas' working vineyards and the Torrontés Wrap using wine yeast and essential oils. Less wholesome but just as indulgent is the massive wine cellar stocked with dozens of Argentina's most notable labels.

QUINTESSENTIALLY INSIDER
Request a private Yoga session on your terrace and practice pranayama whilst gazing out at unimpeded views of the Andes.

Cavas Wine Lodge Costa Flores s/n, Alto Agrelo, Mendoza, Argentina
Tel & Fax: +54 261 410 6927 Email: reservas@cavaswinelodge.com Web: www.cavaswinelodge.com

Bahía Las Balsas, Villa La Angostura, Neuquen, Patagonia, Argentina
Tel: +54 294 449 4308 Fax: +54 294 449 4308 Email: info@lasbalsas.com.ar Web: www.lasbalsas.com

Neuquen | Argentina

Las Balsas

In his seminal book Bruce Chatwin describes Patagonia as 'the uttermost part of the earth', and to this day the stretch of land at the southern most tip of South America still retains an air of exotic mystery. Las Balsas is an intimate lodge in the picturesque town of Villa La Angostura. Cradled by eternally snow-capped mountains and surrounded by forest with the tranquil blue waters of Nahuel Huapi Lake at its feet, it does appear to be the stuff of dreams. Each individually styled room or suite has a view of the lake as well as the hotel's rustic wooden jetty from which guests may take boats to explore the spectacular surrounds. Outdoor activities are abound making it an idyllic destination for energetic guests, but it is also a place to unwind and indulge. The hotel's relaxing spa rises above the lake, offering guests the opportunity for complete recovery. A dedicated team of professionals combined with sophisticated equipment, comfortable salons and a wide variety of techniques and services ensure a feeling of physical and mental wellbeing. Followed with a visit to the wine cellar and tasting lounge where over 150 samples are kept – it doesn't get much better.

QUINTESSENTIALLY INSIDER
You don't want to miss the Shirodara treatment with a Champi Massage. Book it when you check in.

Llao Llao Spa, Av. Ezequiel Bustillo, Bariloche, Río Negro, Argentina
Tel: +54 294 444 5772 Email: spa@llaollao.com Web: www.llaollao.com

Bariloche | Argentina

Llao Llao Spa

When artist and architect Alejandro Bustillo built Argentina's famous Llao Llao Hotel and Resort in 1940 he could not have chosen a more glorious location. Poised on a grassy crest between two impossibly blue lakes and framed by the snow-capped Andes, the rustic Canadian-style property has become something of a national landmark. Over the years it has offered refuge to the most outstanding and prominent figures of Argentine and International society. The hotel philosophy is to value and take advantage of local natural resources, it is evident in the use of regional green stone, the cypress and pine-log walls, the monumental hallway adorned with paintings from local artists as well as the lovely Llao Llao Spa. Here, in the spa treatment rooms, huge picture windows yield stunning views of the magnificent surroundings and the spa menu includes special programmes based on the regenerating and toning properties of rose hip and vita murtilla (both are regional bushes). Other treatment options include a range of facials, the Excellence programme intended to address the signs of ageing, revitalisation and detoxification packages plus fitness hydrotherapy and relaxation programmes.

QUINTESSENTIALLY INSIDER
If you're watching your weight but still want to indulge in the hotel's International cuisine, consult one of the expert nutrition staff. They will carefully assess your needs then plan every meal to produce a perfect combination of health and flavour.

UXUA Casa, Quadrado, Trancoso, Brazil
Tel: +55 733 668 2277 Email: info@uxua.com Web: www.uxua.com

Trancoso | Brazil

UXUA Casa

When Wilbert Das, Creative Director of Italian fashion label Diesel, first visited the colourful, Bohemian town of Trancoso in Bahia (the Edenlike stretch of Brazil's northeast coast boasting music, culture and the best beaches in South America) he immediately knew he wanted to stay. He set to work converting a little house with an over grown garden on the *Quadradro* (village square) into a private retreat. From humble beginnings the project developed and early this year Das opened UXUA (pronounced ooosh-uw-a), a laid-back hotel comprising nine luxury one-, two- or three-bedroom *casas* and a small idyllic spa. Guests can indulge in a variety of wellness and local beauty treatments, including massage and acupuncture, from rustic but very chic indoor or outdoor treatment areas in the enchanting garden. There is a Jacuzzi set in lush greenery plus a studio for Yoga and Pilates. All the buildings and interiors are created in collaboration with local craftsmen using only local and recycled materials so guests are at all times immersed in the Bahian way of life. The environment and the people are immensely restorative and Das describes the place as having "some magic power that is completely relaxing and takes away all the stress".

QUINTESSENTIALLY INSIDER
The beautiful pool is lined with thousands of green aventurine stones which, if you believe in the power of crystals, are supposed to have healing properties… wonderful for the immune system and emotional balance.

Europe

There are few places in the world that have such a rich and well preserved history as Europe. Despite being the second smallest of the continents, with the most temperate climate, Europe still manages to offer travellers a diverse and memorable experience. A mere few hours travelling and you will find yourself in a completely different environment, immersed in a new and exciting way of life. This continent played a huge part in shaping the modern western culture. Early European civilisations have passed down innovations in technology, philosophy, mathematics and science that are still used today.

Europe is widely regarded as the birthplace of the spa industry. The Ancient Greeks were the first people to use sea water as a healing therapy. Their form of treatment, known as Thalassotherapy, literally means 'seawater to cure', and is still used in spas all over the world. The first health spa ever recorded was in a Belgian town, where a fountain of natural spring water was believed to cure all kinds of ailments. European spas maintain a focus on water treatments, also called hydrotherapy, as well as incorporating the natural healing powers of the marine world.

Seaweed, although not exclusively used in Europe, was certainly one of the first ingredients to be added to spa treatments in this part of the world. There are a staggering 35,000 different varieties, each with its own amazing properties. Seaweeds are thought to act in an almost identical way to human skin making them fantastically effective ingredients.

Their list of benefits is endless – from detoxification to deep down hydration, it is easy to see why they are the true heroes of skin care.

Precious oils, such as olive and grape seed, have been added to skincare products for their famous nourishing and moisturising properties. The oils contain a high number of essential fatty acids (needed for the structure of the skin) and plenty of important anti-oxidants, which can help to counteract the damage from free radicals.

Many species of rose are native to Europe. The rose flower symbolises femininity, love, and purity, and has been worshiped in many cultures over the years. It gives us a wealth of useful extracts; from the pure oil used in aromatherapy, known as rose absolute, to the infused floral water that is added to many facial tonics. It has been used to treat sensitive, reactive skins as well as having powerful anti ageing properties. Many, many rose petals are needed to obtain even the tiniest amount of concentrated oil. It is for this reason that, in spa culture, the rose is so highly prized.

The European spa experience is all about elegance, opulence and style. Our guide to the top spas of the region brings you all of this and much more. If you are looking for escapism in the most sophisticated surroundings, we have found it for you.

Blue Lagoon, 240 Grindavík, Iceland
Tel: +354 420 8800 Fax: +354 420 8801 Email: bluelagoon@bluelagoon.is Web: www.bluelagoon.com

Grindavik | Iceland

Blue Lagoon

A visit to The Blue Lagoon is a unique experience; it is easy to see why it is one of Iceland's most popular attractions. The natural geothermal seawater is renowned for its healing power and its unique active ingredients: silica and algae, which cleanse and nourish the skin. In-water massages and spa treatments are based on these active elements and take place in a spacious open-air spa area within the natural lagoon. The signature treatment is an energising massage using the innate white Blue Lagoon silica mud, but salt glow and algae treatments are also on the menu. Before and after, visitors may relax in the warm waters enjoying the crisp, clean air, the invigorating waterfall (a natural hydrotherapy massage), the sauna and the steam bath. Accommodation is available at the Blue Lagoon Clinic – which specialises in the treatment of psoriasis – as well as private changing rooms, an exclusive indoor lagoon and relaxation areas. Modern architecture is in perfect harmony with the natural environment; lava walls and floor-to-ceiling windows provide a strong connection with the surrounding volcanic landscape. A popular restaurant overlooks the lagoon with stunning views across the pools and billowing steam.

QUINTESSENTIALLY INSIDER
Don't leave without picking up some exclusive Blue Lagoon skin care products. Made from the lagoons natural silica mud and algae you can benefit from spa's unique, active elements when you return home.

Monart Destination Spa, The Still, Enniscorthy, Co. Wexford, Ireland
Tel: +353 53 923 8999 Fax:+353 53 923 0944 Email: info@monart.ie Web: www.monart.ie

Wexford | Ireland

Monart Destination Spa

Monart is regarded by many (*Condé Nast Traveller, Tatler* and *Forbes Magazine* included) as one of the world's leading destination spas. Nestled in over 100 acres of Wexford woodland near miles of sandy beach and surrounded by Chelsea Gold Medal-winner Mary Reynolds-designed gardens, Monart is indeed a stunning destination. An original 18th century sandstone manor house, complete with old-world library and living rooms, forms an impressive and elegant entrance. From here, a great glass walkway leads to a spectacular contemporary building sensitively designed with the greatest respect for nature and the environment. Nature is key to the Monart experience, the excessive use of timber and glass provides a deep connection with the surrounding woodland and the hotel's green credentials (energy management system and bio-mass heating) are as impressive as its spa treatments – which use 100% natural Pevonia Botantica products. It is also a seriously technical spa with a state-of-the-art thermal suite including a samarium, caldarium, Kneipp pool, salt grotto, aromatic steam room, hydrotherapy pool, hammam, mud chamber and outdoor traditional Finnish sauna. Guests may choose to embark on Detox, Rewind or Physical Therapy programmes, or simply immerse themselves in the beautiful setting, indulge in the first rate facilities and enjoy the sumptuous meals – all made using locally sourced ingredients.

QUINTESSENTIALLY INSIDER
After a brisk walk in the countryside treat yourself to a generous portion of rich, dark Guinness bread – a Monart speciality.

SAMAS at the Park Hotel Kenmare, Kenmare, Co Kerry, Ireland
Tel: +353 64 664 1200 Fax: +353 64 664 1402 Email: info@parkkenmare.com Web: www.parkkenmare.com

Co Kerry | Ireland

SAMAS Spa

The Park Hotel Kenmare is one of Ireland's foremost privately owned luxury hotels. The Great Southern & Western Railway Company constructed the original limestone building in 1897. In those days the train would stop at Kenmare and the gentry would stay here before travelling onwards. With beautiful terraced gardens and walkways leading down to fields, woods and the lapping waters of Kenmare Bay, it was, and still Is, a heavenly place to take a break from life. In surprising contrast to the main house – rich in high-ceilinged sitting rooms, open fireplaces, original oil paintings, plush furnishings, and museum-worthy antiques -- the hotel's SAMAS spa is a sleek, modern affair with glass walls, slate floors and a mossy roof. But in perfect harmony with its natural surroundings, the spa complements and draws on its spectacular location; an outdoor vitality pool overlooks tall beech trees with nesting crows and open-air hot tubs occupy the Zen gardens. Within the contemporary spa building, six candlelit treatment rooms are reached via glass stairs, there is an impressive 25 metres stainless steel lap pool, a glass cube sauna and Kneipp pool. SAMAS is from the ancient Gaelic word describing an experience of "indulgence of the senses" – and that it does.

QUINTESSENTIALLY INSIDER
In addition to early morning Yoga and meditation classes at the Tai Chi pavilion, the hotel also hosts regular retreats including Yoga, Pilates and Life Enhancing weekends. Check the website for visiting Gurus.

The Dorchester Spa, Park Lane, London, England
Tel: +44 207 319 7109 Fax: +44 207 319 7089 Email: spa@thedorchester.com Web: www.thedorchester.com

London | England

The Dorchester Spa

London's iconic hotel, The Dorchester, stole headlines again earlier this year with the launch of its new Fox-Linton-designed spa at the prestigious Park Lane address. The £3.2 million spa renovation follows the hotel's multimillion-pound refit in 2003 and the opening of the celebrated Alain Ducasse restaurant at The Dorchester in 2007. The Dorchester Spa boasts stunning 1930's inspired interiors with a contemporary twist. Nine treatment rooms (including two double suites) feature ceilings fitted with decorative glass that naturally changes colour with movement. Skin care partners include world-renowned super-facialist Vaishaly, anti-ageing experts Carol Joy London, natural products by Kerstin Florian and miracle mood-enhancers Aromatherapy Associates. Post treatment, hotel guests and day spa visitors may choose to unwind in sumptuous day beds or elegant winged armchairs. Ladies can opt for some nail pampering in the dedicated manicure and pedicure suite while gentleman may visit the traditional Barber Shop. There is also a Royston Blythe hair salon, a fitness studio and state-of-the-art aromatic steam rooms. All who enter will emerge refreshed, uplifted, coiffed, polished and glowing.

QUINTESSENTIALLY INSIDER
Keep in mind the spa's philosophy, "a little of what you love is good for you", when visiting the exclusive Spatisserie, an opulent, but intimate space serving afternoon tea with tempting, bite size cakes, Champagne and spa cocktails.

The Spa at Mandarin Oriental Hyde Park, 66 Knightsbridge, London, England
Tel: +44 207 838 9888 Fax: +44 207 838 9883 Email: molon-spa@mohg.com Web: www.mandarinoriental.com/london/spa

London | England

Mandarin Oriental Hyde Park

Just over the road from Harvey Nics, The Spa at the Mandarin Oriental, London is ideally situated for shopaholics in need of a little respite. Accessed via the hotel lobby, the subterranean haven occupies almost the entire basement. It is an enviable address on the edge of Hyde Park, and its exclusivity is reflected in its clientele: Madonna, Jodie Kidd and Micheal Caine have all been spotted here. Minimalist interiors are sophisticated and confidently understated in jet-black granite. Treatments are similarly serious focusing more on healing than preening. The legendary Mandarin Oriental east meets west rituals are bought as time slots rather than menu treatments. This enables therapists to tailor-make the experience based on a guest's specific spiritual and physical wellbeing at that moment. Before treatments guests may indulge in the spa's impressive 'Heat and Water Oasis': crystal steam room, vitality pool, sanarium (cooler than a sauna and less drying) and various showers. Then relax on a bespoke Azumi bed in a very Zen colour therapy room with a cup of exotic herbal tea.

QUINTESSENTIALLY INSIDER
Try one of the Mandarin Oriental's newly launched signature spa therapies. Developed in consultation with specialists in Traditional Chinese Medicine and master aromatherapists, each ritual is tailored to your individual needs.

Cowshed Clarendon Cross, 119 Portland Road, London, England
Tel: +44 207 078 1944 Fax: +44 207 727 9357 Email: reception@cowshedclarendoncross.com Web: www.cowshedonline.com

London | England

Cowshed Clarendon Cross

From humble beginnings as a bespoke range of natural products developed exclusively for the spa (a former cowshed) at Babington House, Cowshed Clarenden Cross is the brand's first stand alone spa. Located in London's Holland Park, die-hard urbanites and dedicated Cowshed fans can enjoy a full range of treatments, including the popular Cowgroom treatment (Cowshed's version of the four hand massage), without having to leave town. Dubbed the 'rural retreat in the city', candlelit treatment rooms have a groovy guitar soundtrack and the welcoming reception area is styled like a farmhouse kitchen. Light lunches, fresh smoothies, coffee and brownies are available from a daily menu. Ilse Crawford-designed interiors include a ground floor nail salon filled with chic white leather armchairs for spa-goers to indulge in a spot of sociable grooming and a glass of Champagne (or click onto Sky TV if not in a gossiping mood). There is also a shop stocking the coveted Cowshed products – all fairtrade and fashionably free from parabens, petrochemicals, sulphates and artificial additives; and still containing some ingredients handpicked from Babington's Victorian walled garden.

QUINTESSENTIALLY INSIDER
The kitchen makes a great venue for a drinks or dinner party; combine with a treatment for the ultimate girly night of eating, drinking and pampering.

Bliss Spa

London | England

Bliss, the cult day spa from New York, opened its doors in London in 2001 and immediately made headlines with its signature Triple Oxygen Treatment Facial. The treatment, which ends with a blast of oxygen over the face, is as good as ever and remains a firm favourite amongst the stars who regularly indulge pre-premiere. Bliss is hip and sassy; the ground floor check-in point and nail bar (where your nails can be soaked in hot cream) is buzzing to a groovy jazz soundtrack and round-the-clock screenings of *Sex And The City*. Downstairs, the low-key lounge area offers a tempting menu of fresh fruit smoothies and chocolate brownies for tucking into pre- and post-treatment. Eight multi-purpose treatment rooms, all pristine white and simply designed (like the rest of the spa), have heated beds and more up-beat music than many establishments. An array of unique treatments includes the indulgent hot milk and almond pedicure, a medley of deep-tissue massages, radical cellulite-fighting wraps and the obligatory Brazilian that, thanks to Bliss' custom-made wax formula, is practically painless.

QUINTESSENTIALLY INSIDER
Bliss offers an impressive range of facials designed for various occasions, skin types and budgets. But if you can't make your mind up, Bliss has devised an ingenious 'build-on' menu: book a basic and then customise the experience as you go along.

Bliss, 60 Sloane Ave, London, England
Tel: +44 207 590 6146 Web: www.blisslondon.co.uk

Leicestershire | England

Ragdale Hall Health Hydro and Thermal Spa

Ragdale Hall is a lovely country manor spa with a friendly and laid-back atmosphere in the rolling Leicester countryside. Voted Best European Destination Spa in the *Professional Beauty Awards* 2007, facilities are first rate and Ragdale Hall has since opened a new multi-million-pound Thermal Spa. Lavish facilities include twelve different hydro and heat areas – a veritable indoor (and outdoor) playground – including ice fountain, colour-flow cave, volcanic salt bath, rose scented sauna, bubbling footbaths and various relaxing pools. It is easy to while away a few hours here. The range of treatments is also extravagant with 50 treatment rooms and around 120 therapists offering a huge choice of standard and completely unique experiences. Residential and day guests tend to float about in fluffy white robes from dawn 'till dusk this, combined with Ragdale Hall's charming Victorian architecture, gives an air of old-fashioned health retreat. However, breakfast in bed, superb customer service, plush interiors and good healthy fare puts pay to any thoughts of deprivation.

QUINTESSENTIALLY INSIDER
Come rain or shine, don't miss the opportunity to swim under the stars as the mist rises from the outdoor waterfall pool. Numerous bays and inlets provide privacy and at the far end a waterfall gives a great head and shoulder massage.

Ragdale Hall Health Hydro and Thermal Spa, Ragdale Village, Nr Melton Mowbray, Leicestershire, England
Tel: +44 166 443 3000 Fax: +44 166 443 3044 Email: reservations@ragdalehall.co.uk Web: www.ragdalehall.co.uk

Sequoia at The Grove, Chandler's Cross, Hertfordshire, England
Tel: +44 192 329 4214 Fax: +44 192 329 4296 Email: sequoia@thegrove.co.uk Web: www.thegrove.co.uk

Hertfordshire | England

Sequoia at The Grove

The Grove is an impressive 18th century mansion house 30km from central London. Former home of the Earls of Clarendon, weekend parties here were regularly attended by Queen Victoria. Today, The Grove has been sensitively restored to create an elegantly hip rural retreat where antiques are displayed alongside modern art and visitors remain suitably eminent. The spa, Sequoia, is located in the estate's original stable block and mirrors the main hotel with its lavish yet strikingly contemporary décor. The stunning 22 metre swimming pool is lined with black mosaic tiles and the candlelit cocoon-like relaxation room is bedecked in aubergine coloured velvet. State-of–the-art facilities include a crystal steam room, scented mist or tropical rain showers, a sauna and a therapeutic saline vitality pool tucked discreetly away in a slate-grey cavern. The clean lines and oiled-oak floors of the fitness and exercise studios are flooded with natural light from the spa's inner courtyard. There is a sunken ornamental garden open to the sky with glass doors that can be pulled back in summer months. ESPA treatments are tailor-made to your mood and needs, there is even a treatment designed specifically for golfers to unwind after a day on The Grove's championship golf course.

QUINTESSENTIALLY INSIDER
Sequoia is one of only a few spas in the world to offer ESPA Ayurvedic treatments. These wonderful dosha specific rituals include a *Padabhyanga* foot treatment, exfoliation polarity balancing and a specialised face and body massage. The rituals end with a blissful Indian head massage or Shirodhara oil pouring.

Pennyhill Park Hotel and The Spa, London Road, Bagshot, Surrey, England
Tel: +44 127 647 1774 Fax: +44 127 647 3217 Email: enquiries@pennyhillpark.co.uk Web: www.exclusivehotels.co.uk

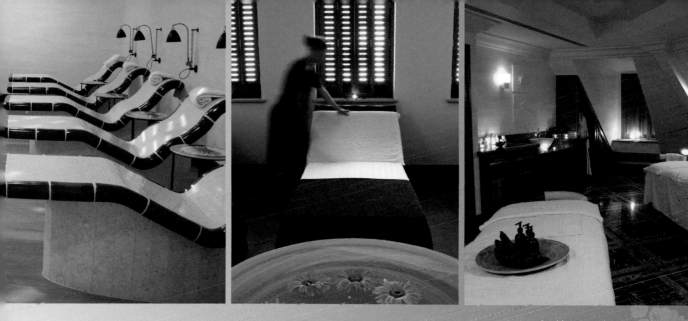

Surrey | England

Pennyhill Park Hotel

Just 45 minutes from London, Pennyhill Park is an elegant ivy-clad country retreat that takes its spa-ing seriously. Beyond the sweeping driveway and the 19th century mansion (housing 123 individually designed bedrooms) lays a huge indoor and outdoor sanctuary voted 'Best Hotel Spa' at the *European Health and Spa Awards* 2009. The spa area is so large it takes a map to negotiate, but the relaxing ambiance and helpful staff make it a pleasure to explore. An astonishing eight pools in total (all ozone treated – so no chemical nasties) include the spa's centerpiece: a 25 metre blue ballroom swimming pool with underwater music. Outside there are bubbling Canadian hot tubs and hydrotherapy pools. Twenty-one therapy rooms offer a massive range of treatments using The Spa own brand products as well as Li'Tya and Terraké. Treatments encompass relaxation, beatification and purification; there are options for men, options for mothers-to-be plus a range of alternative therapies to choose from. In addition, The Spa at Pennyhill Park boasts the UK's most advanced thermal sequencing experience with herbal saunas, laconium, tepidarium, ice cave, aromatic schnapps steam rooms and foot massage thrones. A golf course, a tennis court, a Michelin-starred restaurant and 120 acres of rolling Surrey countryside complete the utterly indulgent experience.

QUINTESSENTIALLY INSIDER
Make time for a workout in the fantastically equipped gym and keep your eyes peeled for the England Rugby Team – this is where they come to train.

U Spa, Hotel Fouquet's Barrière, 46 Avenue George V, Paris, France
Tel: +33 140 696 000 Fax: +33 140 696 005 Email: UHFB@lucienbarriere.com Web: www.fouquets-barriere.com

Paris | France

U Spa

U Spa is a chic sanctuary on the lower level Hôtel Fouquet's Barrière, Paris' new Jacques Garcia-designed five star hotel. The location is cliché-perfect on the corner of the Champs-Elysées with its Art Déco entrance on the designer boutique-lined Avenue George V (alongside the legendary restaurant Fouquet's - the hotel's namesake). Glamorous rooms and suites overlook the Arc de Triomphe or the Eiffel Tower and, with one butler to every eight guests, service is of the best in the city. The spa is set around a large pool – a rarity in Paris – with a lavish aqua-slimming trail involving bubbles, jets and waterfalls. Light billowy curtains divide the space – a sophisticated mix of slate tiles, pale woods and rich mosaics. U Spa signature therapies include a wide array of body, facial and beauty treatments administered in one of seven individually designed treatment rooms. There is also a sauna, a steam room and a sleek fitness facility with personal trainers to hand out the motivation.

QUINTESSENTIALLY INSIDER
Check out the hotel's Sparis package – a cosseting two-night stay for two people including treatments, healthy meals and personal fitness coaching.

Le Spa, Park Hyatt Paris-Vendôme

Le Spa on the basement floor of Park Hyatt Paris-Vendôme is a chic sanctuary of warm wood and cool limestone reserved exclusively for guests of the hotel. A delicate aroma of East Indian lemongrass, eucalyptus and Brazilian orange waft throughout communal areas and Blaise Mautin, the hotel's perfumer, creates unique scents specific to each treatment. There is a balneotherapy and whirlpool area, hammam and steam rooms plus state-of-the-art-gym. In four treatment rooms, including one double, a team of masseurs customise Californian, Swedish, Thai or hot stone therapies to guest's individual needs. The hotel is a grand conversion of five belle-époque houses on the fashionable Rue de la Paix. Despite a discreet mahogany entrance – which one might easily pass by – interiors offer high ceilings, colonnades and inner courtyards. Cool contemporary interiors by American Ed Tuttle (the designer responsible for cutting-edge Amanresorts), however, give the hotel a Zen vibe that differentiates it from more classic neighbours.

QUINTESSENTIALLY INSIDER
To enjoy a private spa experience, opt for one of the hotel's three Presidential Suites. These huge spaces, luxuriously decorated in mahogany, oak and chenille silk, feature Insuite Spas with whirlpool baths, steam rooms and treatment tables.

Guerlain, Trianon Palace, 1 Boulevard de la Reine, Versailles, France
Tel: +33 130 845 140 Fax: +33 130 845 141 Email: spa.trianon@spachakra.com Web: www.trianonpalace.com

Trianon Palace

Just 20km from the centre of Paris, France's leading luxury retreat, the newly updated Trianon Palace Versailles, boasts the city's largest spa facility. This is where fashionable Parisians and international guests come to be preened, pampered and styled. Nestled on the edge of the tranquil Royal Domain amid centuries-old trees, the modern spa is steeped in history. Arranged over three levels, 14 spacious treatment rooms, a hair salon and a fitness centre surround the hotel's 200 metre sq indoor pool. Modelled after a royal Grecian bathhouse, the pool is the spa's jewel in its crown. Dappled sunlight filters down across the water from a second-story solarium, while oversized windows offer views of the hotel's lush, vivid gardens by famous landscape designer Louis Benech. Prestigious skin care experts Guerlain run the spa and skilled beauty therapists begin each treatment with a personal analysis and skin diagnosis. Therapies are then transformed into unique and personal occasions tailored according to individual needs using the wonderful Guerlain products.

QUINTESSENTIALLY INSIDER
For an experience that leaves you in a haven of serenity and voluptuous pleasure opt for the new two-hour Signed by Guerlain treatment – pure bliss for both face and body.

The Spa, Four Seasons Provence, Domaine de Terre Blanche, Tourrettes, Var, France
Tel: +33 494 399 000 Fax: +33 494 399 001 Email: reservations.provence@fourseasons.com Web: www.fourseasons.com

Provence | France

Four Seasons Provence at Terre Blanche

The Spa at the all-suite Four Seasons Resort Provence is located in a lovely two-storey Provençal villa surrounded by the unmistakable sights, sounds and smells of the region. It is jaw-dropingly grand; included among the best spas in *Condé Nast Traveller's* 'Hot Spa List' last year. Fourteen modern treatments rooms, including two couple suites, have huge windows or private terraces overlooking an exquisite garden of cypress and olive trees. Treatments use ESPA, Terraké and Sodashi, with each ritual individually tailored by skilled therapists. In addition to the resort's outdoor infinity-edge pool, which drops off the hillside to far reaching views of medieval villages and soft-scented lavender fields, the spa boasts a dramatic black granite pool flanked by dazzling white columns. The gym is top-notch with state-of-the-art cellulite-busting equipment and a Zen studio for Yoga and Pilates. Outdoor exercise is provided by the resort's Dave Thomas-designed 18-hole golf course and two floodlit tennis courts. There is a vitality pool and separate male and female relaxation areas with sauna, steam room, laconium and ice fountain for cooling off. A pedicure and manicure studio plus a hair salon take care of the finishing touches.

QUINTESSENTIALLY INSIDER
Arrive at least 30 minutes before your treatment to relax in the outside vitality pool. Alone with sound of birdsong and the scent of lavender, thyme and mimosa filling the air, the stress of everyday life will melt away.

Spa Imperial, HOTEL DU PALAIS, 1 Avenue de l'Impératrice, Biarritz, France
Tel: +33 559 416 400 Fax: +33 559 416 799 Email: spa@hotel-du-palais.com Web: www.hotel-du-palais.com

Biarritz | France

Spa Imperial

The Spa Imperial at Hotel du Palais, Biarritz, is an extravagant 2,900 metre sq of lavish, light-filled space dedicated to wellness, fitness and relaxation. Napoléon III originally built the magnificent hotel as a summer mansion for his wife Eugénie, and it has remained the grand playground of the international elite for over a century; Coco Chanel, Ava Gardner and Frank Sinatra have all stayed here. Located on Miramar Beach between the iconic lighthouse and the Grande Plage, the hotel dominates the coast with its ageless charm. Antique furnishings and shimmering chandeliers adorn the foyer and the spa is no less palatial. The beautiful indoor pool stretches out between white marble pillars to large windows with marvellous views of the Atlantic. There are two saunas, two steam rooms, a Jacuzzi and a fully equipped fitness studio (private Yoga and Pilates classes can be arranged on request). Even the spa café, Le Salon Eugénie, serves Champagne. Luxurious treatments are offered in association with Guerlain, Paris (the anti-ageing experts), there is a Léonor Greyl hair care salon and Wellbeing Consultants are on hand to prescribe personal treatment programmes.

QUINTESSENTIALLY INSIDER
The hotel's outdoor pool, just steps from the beach, is filled with heated seawater. Make time to camp out in one of the pool's private cabanas and gaze out over the sand to the rolling waves beyond.

La Réserve Spa, La Réserve Ramatuelle Hotel Spa and Villas, Chemin de la Quessine, Ramatuelle, France
Tel: +33 494 449 444 Fax: +33 494 449 445 Email: inforamatuelle@lareserve.ch Web: www. lareserve.ch

La Réserve

Saint Tropez's latest luxhole is the Jean-Michel Wilmotte-designed La Réserve Ramatuelle. Opened earlier this year it is the third property from the sophisticated 'La Réserve Hospitality Collection' which also boasts pads in Geneva and Paris. The unabashedly modern 23-room hotel, just minutes from the legendary town, is set within an exclusive and private realm with unending views of the Med. But it's the extravagant 1,000 metre sq spa that sets this property apart. Dedicated to enhancing youth, beauty and wellbeing (without needles), the spa offers a 'total-care' approach built around four major goals – stress reduction, fitness, slimming and beauty. Personalised programmes encompass hydrotherapy, fangotherapy (an innovative energising treatment), body care treatments, anti-ageing facials, relaxation and physical fitness. Awash with strong lines and strikingly contemporary features, the spa has 13 treatment rooms, indoor and outdoor pools, a steam bath and a fitness centre.

QUINTESSENTIALLY INSIDER
The hotel rooms and suites are both spacious and private, but for ultimate escapism opt for one of the properties original Rémi Tessier-designed villas. With between four and six bedrooms, a private pool and garden, guests can still make use of all the new hotel and spa facilities.

Metropole ESPA Monte-Carlo, 4 Avenue de la Madone, Monaco
Tel: +377 9315 1370 Fax: +377 9315 1371 Email: receptionespa@metropole-espa.com Web: www.metropole.com

Metropole ESPA Monte Carlo

Bringing together the spa experts at ESPA, the celebrated interior designer Jacques Garcia, the superstar chef Joël Robuchon and a choice location at the heart of Monaco's famous Carré d'Or, the Hotel Metropole Monte-Carlo is the hottest address in town. The grand 146-room hotel just steps from the city's legendary Casino re-opened in 2004 following a total makeover. The opening of an urban destination spa followed just two years later. Spanning three levels, the spa includes 10 mood enhancing treatment rooms, two spacious VIP suites, nurturing heat experiences, fitness facilities and meditative relaxation areas. There is also a private teak wood sun deck and a heated outdoor seawater pool set within gardens. Holistic ESPA treatments combine the best of ancient and modern therapies with top quality ingredients and scientific know-how, each one tailor-made to individual needs. The beautifully designed and well thought out space, the quality of treatments and the exceptional levels of service justify the spa's selection for representation by the Leading Spas of the World – an industry benchmark.

QUINTESSENTIALLY INSIDER
If you're a lover of Sushi, Sashimi, Maki and Sake, don't miss Robuchon's new restaurant YOSHI – which means 'kindness' in Japanese. It opened at Hotel Metropole Monte-Carlo last December and serves a selection of Japanese cuisine from the world's most Michelin starred chef.

Clinique La Prairie, Ch. de la Prairie, 1815 Clarens-Montreux, Switzerland
Tel: +41 219 893 311 Fax: +41 219 893 433 Email: info@laprairie.ch Web: www.laprairie.ch

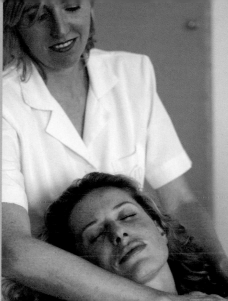

Montreux | Switzerland

Clinique La Prairie

The world renowned Clinique La Prairie on the shores of Lake Geneva was founded in 1931. Its reputation as a medical and beauty spa of the very highest standard and its achievements in specialist areas, such as preventative medicine, health, wellbeing and beauty therapies, have resulted in a stellar client list and multiple awards (including 'Best Destination Spa' *Condé Nast Traveller* (UK) Reader's award 2008). The clinic's philosophy has always been that of dedicated research and the development of techniques to help patients live better and longer lives. The range of services and treatments is one of the most comprehensive in the world, many being exclusive, created by the clinic's own highly trained staff – 60 consultants representing almost every medical and beauty specialisation. An ultra modern spa facility, featuring a heated salt water pool with adjacent sauna and Jacuzzi, was added in 2005 to complement the original 19th century Château. Clients can benefit from personalised treatment programmes (spanning thalassotherapy, weight management, 'Beautymed', bodily rejuvenation, exercise, fitness and relaxation) whilst enjoying a high level of privacy, five star-style accommodation and a magnificent lakeside location.

QUINTESSENTIALLY INSIDER
For a non-surgical solution to wrinkles try La Prairie's signature Simonin treatment. Electric current is applied to the skin through fine needles, this stimulates the skin's natural collagen and improves elasticity, firmness and moisture.

La Réserve Spa, La Réserve Genève Hotel and Spa, 301, Route de Lausanne, Bellevue, Switzerland
Tel: +41 229 595 959 /229 595 999 Fax: +41 229 595 960 Email: spa@lareserve.ch Web: www.lareserve.ch

La Réserve Spa

La Réserve Genève Hotel and Spa is Geneva's first contemporary five star hotel. Set on the shores of the lake, its unassuming exterior gives way to deliciously unexpected and inspirational interiors by star designer Jacques Garcia. In a witty and lateral interpretation of the name 'La Réserve', Garcia's bold creation is reminiscent of a luxurious African safari lodge. In his glamorous spa, colonial-style black rattan loungers surround a sleek indoor pool and a chic spa restaurant features all white leather chairs and tables. There are separate hammams and saunas for male and female guests and a state-of-the-art fitness studio with personal trainers on hand. Water sports on the lake and tennis are also available during the summer months. A broad choice of spa therapies using La Prairie and Cinq Mondes products are offered from 17 treatment rooms. La Réserve signature treatments, aromatherapy, hydrotherapy, Shiatsu, hot stone therapy, reflexology, facials, physiotherapy, body wraps, manicures and pedicures can all be tailored to individual requirements.

QUINTESSENTIALLY INSIDER
Consider enrolling on one of La Réserve Spa's innovative five-day programmes: Better Aging, Detox, Slimming, Anti-stress or Beauty. After a comprehensive body, lifestyle, fitness and medical assessment, a personal results-orientated programme is devised offering practical advice and achievable goals.

Bellevue SPA, Grand Hotel Bellevue, Gstaad, Switzerland
Tel: +41 337 480 101 Fax: +41 337 480 005 Email: wellness@bellevue-gstaad.ch Web: www.bellevue-gstaad.ch

Gstaad | Switzerland

Grand Hotel Bellevue Spa

Following a total refurbishment the once faded Grand Hotel Bellevue in the wealthy Swiss village of Gstaad has raised the bar and is now attracting its own fair share of the great and the good. Set within an idyllic park at the entrance to the village, the Grand Hotel is also a golf retreat, but it's the 2,500 metre sq Asian-style spa that is the star attraction. Modern and minimalist whilst oozing indulgence, the spoiling range of wet facilities are absolutely top-notch. There are seven treatment rooms, a 16 metre indoor pool, a Jacuzzi, a refreshing ice grotto, saunas, immune boosting or aromatherapy steam baths, a salt grotto and a well-equipped gym. The relaxation lounge features heated waterbeds and a large outside sun terrace offers beautiful Alpine views. There is also a new outdoor massage pavilion in the hotel's garden, enabling guests to enjoy the full range of signature massages whilst inhaling the fresh and invigorating mountain air.

QUINTESSENTIALLY INSIDER
After a relaxing session at the spa visit the SPA Bar for a healthy mocktail and freshly made sushi courtesy of Norihiro Ogura, the Bellevue's own Japanese sushi master.

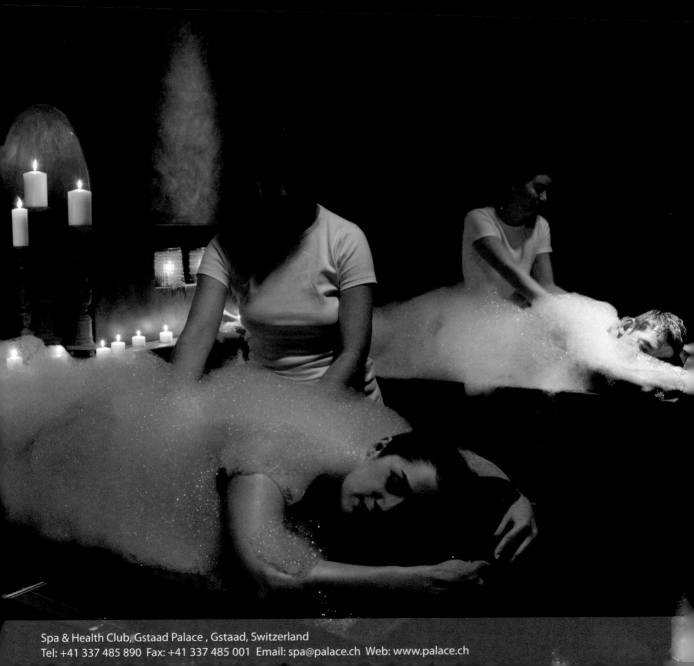

Spa & Health Club, Gstaad Palace , Gstaad, Switzerland
Tel: +41 337 485 890 Fax: +41 337 485 001 Email: spa@palace.ch Web: www.palace.ch

Gstaad | Switzerland

Gstaad Palace

Famous for its glamorous and fabulously wealthy clientele, the iconic Gstaad Palace Hotel sits above the picturesque town of Gstaad in the Swiss Alps. In late 2007, to the tune of £6.5 million, the Hotel opened the doors to a new spa and health club offering guests – the likes of Liza Minnelli, Roman Polanski and Woody Allen – another way to unwind in the mountains. The spa includes eight treatment rooms, a private spa suite, saunas and steam baths, a state-of-the-art gym, a Pilates studio, an indoor pool and an outdoor pool with a Jacuzzi. In a bid to optimise the mountain experience, the space is flanked by a 60 metre-long granite stone wall – over 50 tons of rock cut into small pieces and assembled to create a stunning architectural master piece. Another highlight is the elegant relaxation lounge with a central circular fireplace and spectacular mountain views. From a long list of options, guests might indulge in a Phyto-Aromatic Facial, an Oxypeel Balancing treatment or Manual Lymph Drainage. It's enough to tempt even the most committed skier off the slopes and back to the luxurious surroundings of the hotel.

QUINTESSENTIALLY INSIDER
A unique hammam experience transports guests through seven rooms over the course of two hours. The ritual begins with a soothing foot bath and concludes with a hydrating oil massage. A cleansing soap-foam body massage, a steam bath and a dip into the "Floating Pool" are all included en-route.

The Spa at Mandarin Oriental, Nebovidska, Prague, Czech Republic
Tel: +420 233 088 888 Fax: +420 233 088 668 Email: moprg-reservations@mohg.com Web: www.mandarinoriental.com/prague

Prague | Czech Republic

Mandarin Oriental Prague

The Mandarin Oriental, Prague, needs no introduction and their first venture in Eastern Europe has captured the spirit of the city by locating in a converted Dominican monastery. Vaulted ceilings, Baroque columns and arched windows have all been carefully preserved; guests can appreciate the history of this beautiful city without even leaving the building. The spa is housed in a former Renaissance chapel reached via a 'secret' underground passage (still no reason to venture outside!). On entering the spa, one has a remarkable sense of transcending time and culture. The lobby (the former nave) is vast, filled with light and spectacularly modern with a stunning glass floor. Under the floor are the remains of a one time Gothic church uncovered during the site's reconstruction. Asian touches (reminders of the Mandarin Oriental's origin and philosophy) include the Tea Lounge – the first stop for all treatment sessions. In a different approach to the traditional spa experience guests are encouraged to book 'Time' rather than a specific treatment, this enables therapists to tailor the ritual to the individual's lifestyle, characteristics and preferences. But all treatments begin with a relaxing foot massage that, after pacing the city's cobbles, is an absolute essential - no one really expects you to remain inside.

QUINTESSENTIALLY INSIDER
The De-stress Mind and Body Wrap comes highly recommended. Following a natural body exfoliation, nurturing oils, gels, and creams infused with lavender, rosemary, and ginger envelope the body helping to relieve muscle tension, calm the mind and leave skin glowing.

Sankt Jörgen Park Resort

Gothenburg | Sweden

A few minutes walk from the lively and cosmopolitan centre of Gothenburg, Sankt Jörgen Park Resort is Sweden's first city resort boasting an 82-room design hotel and one of the countries most luxurious spas. Set serenely among parkland, leafy forest and meadows, guests can dip in and out of the nearby city scene – visiting any of the 25 theatres, 18 museums and four Michelin-starred restaurants that Gothenburg has to offer – then retreat back to the sanctuary of the resort. The spa is designed by renowned Swedish spa designer Mikael Becktor, and comprises a paradise of warm, cold and cool pools plus saunas with shifting heat zones and fragrances. Treatments, inspired by nature, span a wide range of holistic massage, facials and body therapies as well as a number of Aurvedic rituals and signature cures – all categorised in the menu as either relaxing, purifying or energising. There are various packages to choose from for groups or individuals, but guests wanting a full spa experience should consider the customised spa rituals, each one with a specific aim: relaxation, vitalisation or pure energy boost.

QUINTESSENTIALLY INSIDER
After a challenging round of golf at the resort's beautiful 18-hole course book in for a Golf Cure at the spa. A warm footbath is followed by a circulation-raising back and shoulder massage.

Sankt Jörgen Park Resort, Gothenburg, Sweden
Tel: +46 313 484 000 Email: info@sanktjorgenpark.se Web: www.sanktjorgenpark.se

Vienna | Austria

Palais Coburg

On the top floor of Vienna's five star, all-suite Palais Coburg, the hotel spa looks out over the rooftops and parks of the city centre. Built in the mid-19th century as the outrageously elegant private home of the Coburg dynasty, the building combines six centuries of architectural history starting with Vienna's original 16th century city walls uncovered and restored in the hotel's basement. But for all its museum-like grandeur the hotel strikes a happy balance between old and new with contemporary urban features alongside restored guilt, antique furnishings and heavy silk drapes. The spa is most definitely of a modern ilk – light and spacious with huge windows and state-of-the-art facilities. Reserved exclusively for guests staying in one of the hotel's 35 suites, the peace and tranquillity is absolute. Massage and beauty treatments use prestigious Maria Galland products, and with a sauna, hammam, whirlpool, generous sized pool with underwater music and a lovely sun terrace, it is an ideal setting for recovery after a tiring day in the city.

QUINTESSENTIALLY INSIDER
The Palais Coburg wine collection, stored in the building's medieval vaults, dates back four centuries. Sample some of the greats at events held every other Wednesday. Check before you book.

Palais Coburg Residenz, Coburgbastei 4, Vienna, Austria
Tel: +43 151 8180 Fax: +43 151 81 8100 Email: hotel.residenz@palais-coburg.com Web: www.palais-coburg.com

Mayr & more, Golfhotel at Worthersee, Golfstrasse 2, Maria Wörth-Dellach, Carinthia, Austria
Tel: +43 4273 2511 Fax: +43 427 325 1151 Email: ilana@360travel.co.uk Web: www.mayrandmore.at

Carinthia | Austria

Mayr & more

As health spas go, Mayr & more is the real deal. Based on the belief that a healthy intestine is the key to our wellbeing, a stay here involves correct nutrition, exercise, specialist massages, hydrotherapy, blood checks, intravenous infusions and plenty of good old-fashioned rest. The benefits are extolled by dramatic lasting results and returning guests – who leave after the recommended three weeks with younger, healthier, more vibrant looking skin and increased energy levels. The Mayr cure cleanses the body of toxins and can be used to overcome various ailments, prevent surgeries, achieve weight loss or boost the immune system. The ultimate goal is to encourage lifestyle changes that lead to a much healthier and happier life free from physical or mental illness. Dr. F X Mayr developed the famous cure at the turn of the last century, and the clinic was opened over 30 years ago under the medical supervision of one of his most famous pupils, Dr Erich Rauch. Today, his truly holistic approach has become the preventative health care choice among many of European's elite. In addition to the Mayr cure, the clinic offers a wide range of complementary and aesthetic treatments such as Shiatsu, mesotherapy and carboxyterapy, which help address external problems such as posture, cellulite and skin imperfections.

QUINTESSENTIALLY INSIDER
If you don't have three weeks to spare try the one-week introductory Mayr programme which, when combined with The Organic Pharmacy's three week at home detox programme, can still achieve results.

Spa Alpin, Alpenpalace Deluxe Hotel & Spa Resort, Gisse 83, San Giovanni in Valle Aurina, Italy
Tel: +39 047 467 0230 Fax: +39 047 467 1156 Email: info@alpenpalace.com Web: www.alpenpalace.com

Dolomites | Italy

Alpenpalace Deluxe Hotel & Spa Resort

In winter Hotel & Spa Resort Alpenpalace is surrounded by the ski slopes of the South Tyrolean Dolomites; in summer the beautiful Ahrn Valley transforms into a blossoming paradise of green pastures. Spa Alpin is set in seven-and-a-half acres of private parkland complete with Baroque rose garden and tranquil water features. A large outdoor swimming pool is reached via a heated flagstone path and can be enjoyed even on the coolest of mornings. Nearby, a warm whirlpool is perfect for viewing the Dolomites' famous pink sunsets. More pools with waterfalls and massage zones are found inside the huge wellness facility; there are freshwater pools, a therapeutic brine pool and even a children's pool with a water slide tucked quietly away behind a glass wall. From eight treatment areas knowledgeable therapists ease tired muscles after a day in the mountains and pamper guests with a wide variety of relaxing, beautifying and detoxifying rituals courtesy of la prairie. There is a salt graduation tower for inhaling beneficial salt particles, a Tyrolean sauna, a herbal bath, a steam bath, a Laconium and an ice fountain. But it's the stunning mountain scenery and the contemporary, Alpine style interiors complete with comforting open fires which sets this five star resort and spa apart.

QUINTESSENTIALLY INSIDER
Book one of the new spa suites for romantic body and beauty treatments together with your partner.

L'Albereta Espace Vitalité, Henri Chenot Via Vittorio Emanuele II n°23, Erbusco (BS), Italy
Tel: +39 030 776 0550 Fax: +39 030 776 0573 Email: info@albereta.it Web: www.albereta.it

Erbusco | Italy

L'Albereta

Typical of Italy, L'Albereta is a spa hotel that has its priorities right. Set among the undulating vine covered hills of the Franciacorta region, the hotel's private wine cellar is packed with world class vintages (including the local sparkling white) and the restaurant is run by legendary Italian chef, Gualtiero Marchesi. Henri Chenot heads the Spa at L'Albereta. Also a leader in his field, Chenot is as serious about health as Marchesi is about food (guests on one of Chenot's spa packages are advised to stick to the diet menus). Chenot believes that by re-balancing our own vital energy, we can achieve optimum wellbeing (*benessere*) and, at the same time, resist the ageing process. All Chenot's programmes begin with bio-energetic testing; guests are wired to a computer via their 'energy points', and the results, Chenot claims, reveal the body's toxins. The first stage of the treatment entails relaxation and detox via diet and hydrotherapy. One whole floor of the two level spa is given over to hydrotreatments, dominated by a huge swimming pool equipped with five different types of hydromassage. The second phase is devoted to regeneration. This involves beauty treatments and whole body massages using natural products rich in vitamins and minerals. The benefits after just a few days are striking: guests leave feeling more relaxed, more toned and lighter with re-hydrated skin and luminous complexions – possibly the reason why L'Albereta is so popular with the local Milanese.

QUINTESSENTIALLY INSIDER
Fitness is a key part of Chenot's method and the Franciacorta region, one of Italy's least explored areas, offers the perfect opportunity to get out on foot, bike or horseback and discover the lush and beautiful countryside.

Bauer Palladio SPA, Giudecca 33 , Venice, Italy
Tel: +39 041 520 7022 Fax: +39 041 520 7557 Email: booking@bauervenezia.com Web: www.bauerhotels.com

Venice | Italy

Bauer Palladio SPA

A contender for the title of 'spa with the best view', Bauer Palladio (Venice's newest holistic wellness spa) is located on Giudecca Island, across the water from St. Mark's Square. Eight treatment rooms and a relaxation lounge boast the most exceptional picture-postcard view of the lagoon and the shores of Venice. The hotel and spa is housed on the water's edge (next door to Elton John) in a 16th century former convent originally designed by world-renowned Renaissance architect Andrea Palladio. The building has been carefully restored and updated under the personal care of interior designer and owner Francesca Bortolotto Possati. The result is a serene retreat where visitors can escape the bustle of Venice, relax in the garden or enjoy a meal 'alfresco' on the tranquil patio. The spa, which features a king-size Turkish hammam, an innovative Vitalis Multi-Bath System and a double size Jacuzzi, is open to guests staying at any of Venice's three Bauer hotels (the Palladio, Il Palazzo overlooking the Grand Canal and the original L'Hotel) – a complimentary solar-powered boat shuttles spa-goes across the water throughout the day. Choose from an array of all-natural wellness therapies designed to de-stress, purify or cleanse whilst taking in that incredible view.

QUINTESSENTIALLY INSIDER
Opt for one of the treatments for which products are mixed together moments before their application – this maximises the full power of the vitamins they contain. The popular clay-based treatments are also particularly effective at drawing impurities from the skin.

Tuscany | Italy   Grotta Giusti Natural Spa Resort

Hidden deep within the Tuscan hills, Grotta Giusti is a 130 million year old cave complete with stalactites, stalagmites and an underground thermal lake. Park your deck chair in Paradise, Purgatory or Hell, depending on your heat preference, and allow the detoxifying vapours, rich in calcium, bicarbonate, sulphur and magnesium, to miraculously sooth joint pains and rejuvenate the soul. The grotta was discovered in 1849 by local labourers, and now forms part of a luxurious natural spa resort developed in the 19th century to indulge such luminaries as Verdi. The main villa, once owned by the poet Giuseppe Giusti (to whom the Grotta owes its name), houses 64 elegant rooms, including six suites, filled with fine furnishings and lavish white marble bathrooms. After experiencing the grotta, guests can indulge in a wide range of healing, relaxing and beautifying treatments from massage to Chinese medicine at the modern Wellness Centre. There is tennis, a gym and, just five minutes away, an 18-hole golf course. Or simply kick back and unwind in the huge outdoor pool fed by the therapeutic thermal waters at 35°C and fitted with underwater hydromassage jets.

QUINTESSENTIALLY INSIDER
Book a Superior or Deluxe room to benefit from the thermal waters on tap, and when fully rejuvenated escape for a spot of retail therapy at some of the nearby outlets.

Fonteverde Natural Spa & Resort, Località Terme I, San Casciano dei Bagni, Siena, Tuscany, Italy
Tel: +39 057 857 241 Fax: +39 057 857 2200 Email: info@fonteverdespa.com Web: www.fonteverdespa.com

Siena | Italy

Fonteverde Natural Spa & Resort

Fonteverde Natural Spa & Resort lies next to the ancient hill town of San Casciano dei Bagni known since ancient times for its thermal springs. The Medici family built their summer retreat here and the hotel, which stands on the same spot, is reminiscent of the aristocratic Tuscan villa that it once was. Frescoed walls and ceilings, elegant porticos and ancient artefacts found during the redevelopment of the hotel juxtapose the glass-walled pools and modern touches. The views from the spa, punctuated by olive groves, vineyards and streams, are among the most beautiful in the region. The local mineral waters are rich in sulphate, calcium, magnesium and fluoride, and well out of the ground at a comfortable 37°C feeding Fonteverde's six therapeutic pools (plus one for dogs). Water is certainly the central theme here, but Fonteverde is more than just a gorgeous luxury spa; a serious range of treatments, massage, therapies and water circuits are on offer as well as consultations that follow the principles of traditional Chinese medicine. Other specialist areas include bio-energetics, dermatology, diet and osteopathy. A host of signature treatments, including the Ancient Mediterranean Thalaquam, Salidarium, Biobalancing, Equilibrium and Thalaquam Massages, use the spas own range of products made from local thermal mud.

QUINTESSENTIALLY INSIDER
Don't leave without experiencing a famous massage from Dipu, the Ayurvedic practitioner and star of this spa. His powerful touch and empathetic personality has a coterie of Italian models, politicians and film stars returning time and time again.

185

ESPA at L'Andana, Tenuta la Badiola, Località Badiola, Castiglione della Pescaia, Tuscany, Italy
Tel: +39 056 494 4800 Fax: +39 056 494 4577 Email: espa@andana.it Web: www.andana.it

Grosseto | Italy

ESPA at L'Andana

Superstar chef and restaurateur Alain Ducasse teamed up with world-renowned spa innovator ESPA to create L' Andana, a 33-room gastronomic retreat dedicated to wellness and gastronomic indulgence. Housed in a former summer residence of Duke Leopold II near Tuscany's fashionable Maremma coast, Ducasse's vision to relax the body and soul whilst awakening the senses is realised. Working with his pastry chef and the experts at ESPA, Ducasse has complemented each treatment with a delicious culinary experience – a particular cake, a mousse or a tart and a fresh herbal tea. The Life-saving Back Massage, for example, is followed by the dark-chocolate mousse; and a soya milk pannacotta with seasonal fruits is recommended after an Intensive Facial. Each experience links together the natural ingredients of the surrounding area – herbs and fruits for the teas and cakes are plucked from the gardens, while specially designed ESPA treatments use many indigenous botanical resources – marjoram, sage, thyme, basil and lavender. Four treatment rooms include two complete spa suites. An indoor vitality pool, filled with beneficial minerals, is heated to a lazy 37°C. There are two further outdoor pools with typically Tuscan views of cypress trees, olive groves and rolling hills beyond.

QUINTESSENTIALLY INSIDER
Interior designer Ettore Mochetti (editor of Italian AD) has jettisoned Chiantishire clichés in favour of a more urban elegance to create airy and pleasantly understated rooms. Opt for room four, seven or nine for the best views, or room 20 for a gigantic in-room bathtub.

Terme di Saturnia Spa & Golf Resort, Saturnia (Grosseto),Tuscany, Italy
Tel: +39 056 460 0111 Fax: +39 056 460 1266 Email: info@termedisaturnia.it Web: www.termedisaturnia.it

Tuscany | Italy

Terme di Saturnia Spa & Golf Resort

Saturnia is no newcomer to the healing game. Since Roman times piping hot sulphurous water has been bubbling out of the ground at a rhythm of 800 litres per second, and 3,000 years ago Etruscan warriors bathed here to help heal their wounds. Today, the natural elements have been combined with the man-made to create Terme di Saturnia Spa & Golf Resort, an elegant hotel with a distinctly holiday feel. Located in the heart of Maremma, southern Tuscany, every element inspires wellbeing; from the beautiful Tuscan hills that map out the horizon to the delicious Italian cuisine and the soothing waters thought to ease or cure all manner of ailments. Massages, beauty treatments and wellbeing programmes are based on Mediterranean traditions with various mud therapies, inhalations and baths taking full advantage of the springs. The Thermal Plankton body or face mask, for example, is made from the slimy plankton that arises from the sulphuric water – it is considered the beauty treatment of the Gods and leaves skin feeling wonderful. But, with 60 treatment rooms, Terme di Saturnia is a medical facility as well as a spa. Countless health professionals with specialities ranging from dermatology to dietology and aestethic medicine are on call to consult and analyse. You can also play golf of course.

QUINTESSENTIALLY INSIDER
Want to prolong your psychophysical youth? Try one of the exclusive and rejuvinating Saturnia Gold Facial or Saturnia DNA Facial treatments, immersed in the dreamy and private atmosphere of the newly inaugurated Blackrose Spa.

189

Daniela Steiner Spa at Romeo, 45 Via Cristoforo Colombo, Naples, Italy
Tel: +39 081 017 5008/9 Fax: +39 081 017 5999 Email: reservations@romeohotel.it Web: www.romeohotel.it

Naples | Italy

The charming city of Naples, typically bypassed by travellers heading south to the Almalfi coast, is fast becoming recognised as a destination in its own right and the new Kenzo Tange-designed Romeo Hotel, which opened earlier this year, is a hot stop for well-healed weekenders. The 85-room hotel at the heart of Naples Harbour combines modern luxury and design (Caprai linen, Antonio Citario B&B furniture and custom-made Philippe Starck sofas) with the city's rich cultural heritage (an impressive collection of works by Naples' hot shot contemporary artists and photographers) and wellness in a stunning 700 metre sq Daniel Steiner spa. In celebration of the Bay of Naples and the majestic Vesuvius that dominate the views from its ninth floor eyrie, the spa is designed with the primordial elements of water and fire in mind. The rooftop hydrotherapy pool seemingly bubbles over into the blue Med below and a fiery Turkish bath area offers an intense relaxing heat. Steiner's unique wellbeing philosophy is brought to life in four treatment rooms where therapies, usually divided into three distinct areas (face, body and feet), are amalgamated into one comprehensive programme. Consultations on arrival are used to determine the type of massage, its duration and the product preparation – a combination of essences and natural ingredients (including algae, clay, salt, herbs and ointments) prepared immediately prior to the treatment.

QUINTESSENTIALLY INSIDER
Don't pass up the offer a fresh fruit juice, this will also have been prepared moments before your arrival in order to maximise the benefits of the vitamins.

Bliss Barcelona, Plaça de la rose del vents 1, Barcelona, Spain
Tel: +34 932 952 800 Fax: +34 913 607 214 Email: wbarcelona.reservations@whotels.com Web: www.whotels.com/barcelona

Barcelona | Spain

Bliss Spa

Hip US spa brand, Bliss, continues its global stampede with the opening of Bliss Barcelona later this year. It will be the second in Europe (outside the UK) with more planned imminently. The venue is the new W Hotel Barcelona at *Nova Bocana* (the 'new entrance') of the Port of Barcelona – an avant-garde sail-shaped structure designed by Barcelona-born and world-renowned architect Ricardo Bofill – also set to debut in the autumn. The 700 metre sq spa will feature treatment rooms, relaxation areas, nail stations, a wet area with steam, sauna, and pool as well as direct access to the beach. Trademark Bliss touches – the fun, up-beat atmosphere, the clever 'tongue-in-cheek' menu, the cool rhythm and blues soundtrack and the legendary brownie buffet – combine with the brands signature services including the famous Blissage75 and Triple Oxygen Facial. The Bliss/ W combo kicked off in 2004 and, in addition to the on-site attitude-free spa experience, hotel guests benefit from perks such as in-room treatments, sink-side skin-care products and W's Whatever/Whenever service.

QUINTESSENTIALLY INSIDER
For beach beautiful toes try Bliss' revolutionary Pedi-Colada a coconut milk soak, a shredded coconut scrub and a hot seashell massage prepare your feet for the perfect polish while you sit back and enjoy a virgin piña colada.

Spa La Posidonia, Hotel Hacienda Na Xamena, San Miguel, Ibiza, Spain
Tel: +34 971 334 500 Fax: +34 971 334 514 Email: info@hotelhacienda-ibiza.com Web: www.hotelhacienda-ibiza.com

Ibiza | Spain

Hotel Hacienda Na Xamena

Set on a 17-acre plot at the heart of a nature reserve – described as one of the last unspoiled ecological environments on the European map, the Hacienda Na Xamena is a luxurious enclave. A sanctuary for well-heeled travellers far removed from Ibiza's maddening crowds and notorious nightlife. This is where the beautiful people come when the party's over. Sixty-five traditional rooms and suites cascade down the hillside to the sparkling emerald sea below. Guests may relax in their own Jacuzzi or mini outdoor swimming pool and admire jaw-dropping views of the dramatic Na Xamena Bay where giant cliffs plunge into the sea to form idyllic pocket-sized coves. The Spa La Posidonia, also built into the cliff side, is open to hotel guests and spa day visitors. It is charmingly rustic with exposed stone and whitewashed walls. But facilities are far from basic: three Vichy showers, two hydro-massage baths, musicotherapy, thalassotherapy and a flotarium are designed to revive and restore mind and body. Facials and beauty treatments are also offered from chic indoor cabins.

QUINTESSENTIALLY INSIDER
Island visitors should not miss Spa La Posidonia´s 'Cascadas Suspendidas', a breathtaking thalasso-trail made of eight hydrotherapy baths which hang on the cliff side 180 metres above sea level (think: Hanging Gardens of Babylon). The pools, connected via waterfalls, are filled with seawater heated to different temperatures and each one massages a different part of the body. Take the circuit at sunset for the ultimate Ibiza chill-out.

Joy Jung Spa, Vila Joya, Praia da Galé, Albufeira, Portugal
Tel: +35 128 959 1795 Fax: +35 128 959 1201 Email: info@vilajoya.com Web: www.vilajoya.com or www.joyjungspa.com

Albufeira | Portugal

Joy Jung Spa

Moroccan arches and twinkling lights; Indian therapists trained in the best Asia establishments; treatments that use fresh herbs and products from The Organic Pharmacy. The Joy Jung Spa at the charming Vila Joya in the central Algarve is a sensational refuge. Just 40 minutes from Faro, Vila Joya is a 20-room, Moroccan-inspired boutique hotel that boasts the only two-Michelin starred restaurant in Portugal. The Joy Jung Spa is a relatively new addition. Based on the elements of water and air, the spa has a golden river and waterfalls flowing throughout the treatment areas and fresh air circulating wherever possible. Outside treatments take place on a floating platform and open air showers offer views of the birds and the stars above. The saunas and steam bath have direct access to Vila Joya's wonderful gardens replete with palm trees, cypresses and agaves. A wide range of massage, scrubs, wraps and facials are available, while Dr Jacob Kurian, the spa's own Ayurvedic specialist, focuses on tailor-made treatments to help cure the body and the mind. There is also a small gym, a Yoga room where complementary classes take place twice a week, two outside pools and an outside Jacuzzi all with magnificent Atlantic Ocean views.

QUINTESSENTIALLY INSIDER
Enjoy an indulgent foot treatment in the open air and surrounded by waterfalls – the therapist treats you with his feet rather than his hands.

Thalassa Spa, Polis, Cyprus
Tel: +35 726 888 000 Fax: +35 726 322 900 Email: spa.anassa@thanoshotels.com Web: www.thanoshotels.com

Polis | Cyprus

The lovely Anassa hotel is built in the style of a Byzantine village on Cyprus' dramatic Akamas Peninsula. Buildings, terraces and three outdoor pools tumble down through lush aromatic gardens to a beautiful sweep of secluded sand below. Anassa's award-winning Thalassa Spa is a tranquil, light-filled space that includes a stunning Roman-style indoor pool flanked by contemporary rattan lounge beds, saunas and steam rooms. It embraces the restorative and rejuvenating qualities of the sea in an extensive thalasso programme incorporating algae wraps and thalassotherapy baths. A wide range of revitalising body and beauty treatments: massage, facials, reflexology, Shiatsu and aromatherapy, use The Organic Pharmacy's 100% natural product line. Lifestyle consulting and acupuncture completes the spa's all-encompassing holistic approach to wellbeing. There is a squash court, a fitness room, a seawater exercise pool plus ample opportunity for water sports in the sparkling Mediterranean.

QUINTESSENTIALLY INSIDER
With the Cyprus weather remaining pleasant and balmy well into November, when it comes to five star winter sun Anassa has the edge on the Med's competition.

Almyra, Poseidonos Avenue , Pafos, Cyprus
Tel: +35 726 888 700 Fax: +35 726 942 818 Email: almyra@thanoshotels.com Web: www.almyra.com

Pafos | Cyprus

Almyra

Almyra is the funky younger sister to Cyprus' grand Anassa hotel. Family friendly and, with rooms from 90 euros a night, it's positively 'new economy'; and it is still, after five years, the hippest place to stay in Cyprus. Last summer the addition of a chic modernist spa complemented the Almyra's existing super cool facilities (a slate-lined freshwater pool, a Japanese-fusion restaurant and a fashionable DJ bar). The new spa is a child free zone of natural wood and slate with all the top-notch trappings – a state-of-the-art gym, water therapy rooms, a mini beauty parlour, a tennis court and a deli-style café. Nine terraced treatment rooms overlook the infinity-edge pool where guest relax on sexy double day beds and the sea laps gently at the surrounding gardens designed by Parisienne Joelle Pleot. Treatments focus on the just pure range of products (exclusive in Cyprus). They contain natural raw ingredients, fresh plant extracts and cold-pressed plant oils all produced according to the rhythms of the moon.

QUINTESSENTIALLY INSIDER
Yummy mummies can take advantage of Almyra's fantastic childcare facilities and escape with hubby to the gorgeous couples suite with treatment facilities, an outside deck and a private garden.

Le Spa, Le Meridien Limassol Spa and Resort, Limassol, Cyprus
Tel: +35 725 863 100 Fax: +35 725 634 112 Email: lespa.limassol@lemeridien.com Web: www.cyprus.lemeridien.com

Le Meridien Limassol Spa and Resort

Cyprus boasts a number of world-class spas with a notable emphasis on the practice of thalassotherapy. The award-winning spa at Le Meridien Limassol Spa and Resort is both the biggest on the island and unique in Europe for its combination of thalassotherapy and other pampering treatments. Set on a rocky cove busy with palm trees, pools, grottos and waterfalls, the spa has four outdoor and three indoor saltwater pools each with a different salinity content and temperature. There are also saunas, whirlpools and a hammam, plus 34 treatment rooms offering no less than 120 different treatments and packages. Fortunately the spa's team of experienced consultants from around the world are on hand to offer guidance and discuss individual requirements. Treatments use Thalgo products, derived from the sea, or Elemis spa products as well as a large amount of seawater and therapeutic mud. The hotel is also renowned for its fantastic children's facilities enabling parents to get away and relax in the all-adult pool or indulge in an all day spa session.

QUINTESSENTIALLY INSIDER

For a truly Cypriot experience opt for a signature Journey of The Senses in which warm volcanic stones collected from the shores of Cyprus are used to give balance, energy and relieve tension. It is followed by a dousing in milk and frangipani oil – an age-old island tradition to moisturise and nourish sun-kissed skin.

Spa Villas with private pools and Elixir Spa Gallery, Elounda Gulf Villas & Suites. Elounda, Crete, Greece
Tel: +30 284 109 0300 (UK Reservation: 0871 990 3010) Fax: +30 281 022 7811 Email: info@eloundavillas.com
Web: www.eloundavillas.com

Crete | Greece

Elounda Gulf Villas & Suites

The Elounda Gulf Villas & Suites is a member of Small Luxury Hotels of the World and the winner of Greece's Leading Villa Award. It is a family-owned and run boutique villa-hotel on Crete's northern coast; a popular choice for celebrities, royals and those who seek privacy combined with first class, tailor-made services. There are 10 elegant suites and 18 individual villas with floor-to-ceiling glass windows and stunning views across the Gulf of Mirabello. All the villas have private pools with Jacuzzis and many also include a private spa with gym room, sauna and steam bath. Therapists are on call to perform curing and relaxing treatments so there is really no need to venture further than your private pool terrace – a spa junkie could want for little more. If you do, however, decide to visit the hotel's Elixir Spa Gallery you will find a fully equipped gym room where personal trainers can be appointed to design or continue a fitness regime. Private Yoga and Pilates sessions can also be arranged. There is an outdoor Jacuzzi, a massage room, additional sauna and steam bath facilities and a large seasonally heated swimming pool. The spa service is special, as is that of the hotel in general – nothing here seems to be too much trouble.

QUINTESSENTIALLY INSIDER
Younger guests don't have to miss out on the pampering experience; the Elixir spa offer a special massage for babies and children using local Cretan olive oil, chamomile and/or aloe vera – book one before bedtime to be sure of a peaceful night.

Elixir Spa & Ayurveda, Amirandes Grecotel Exclusive Resort, Kato Gouves, Heraklion, Greece
Tel: +30 289 704 1103 Email: reserve_am@grecotel.gr Web: www.amirandes.com

Crete | Greece

Elixir Spa & Ayurveda

From the same family who own the off-beat Baby Grand hotel in Athenes, Amirandes Resort on the north coast of Crete has a more classic aesthetic inspired by the sprawling palaces of ancient Minonian Kings. But it is no less striking. Sparking lagoons swirl around the resort lapping at the building's slender wood pillars and natural stone terraces before appearing to merge with the teal blue Mediterranean. This endless water, together with the blazing architecture and minimalist interiors, creates an overwhelming sense of calm; and Amirandes offers ample opportunity for relaxation. The resort's Elixia Spa is a haven of tranquillity – all soft lighting, chakra-balancing music and scented candles. But Elixia is also a spa with a serious Ayurvedic offering. Following a consultation with the in-house Ayurvedic doctor, treatments are tailor-made using customised products and performed by specialist Indian therapist from individually designed treatment suites. There is also a sauna and a lovely indoor pool. For further repose kick back on a pale wood lounger on the long stretch of private sandy beach, or sip coffee beside the Olympic-sized outdoor pool whilst admiring the archway – framed views.

QUINTESSENTIALLY INSIDER
Opt for a sea view room in the principal hotel building where indulgent details extend to private gyms and bathrooms with colour therapy and aromatherapy Jacuzzi tubs. Alternatively, choose a beachside villa with a private pool.

Domes of Elounda Spa, All Suites and Villas Spa Resort, Elounda Lasithi, Crete, Greece
Tel: +30 231 081 0624 Fax: +30 231 081 0634 Email: info@domesofelounda.com Web: www.domesofelounda.com

Crete | Greece

Domes of Elounda Spa

Domes of Elounda is set on a peaceful hillside on the shores of Elounda – Crete's internationally renowned hotspot. Spectacular views of the Med and the island of Spinalonga are all around – from the 84 villas and suites, from the large main pool and from the breathtaking spa. The resort is named because of its unique architecture characterised by smooth domes and pyramid rooves that blend with the natural environment – features borrowed from Greek, Carpathian and Syrian design. But the traditional, organic-shaped rooms are filled with works of art and modern furnishings to give an air of contemporary luxury. As guests enter the Milfey spa, they are welcomed with a black mosaic seawater pool surrounded by floor-to-ceiling windows and objects and furniture from Moroso, Serralunga and Bonaldo; Martinelli Luce light fixtures hover above. Spa treatments are given in womb-like caverns of black and gold mosaic where therapists combine modern techniques with the methods of the ancient Greeks – a culture that set the standard for modern spa procedures over 3,000 years ago. Traditional boundaries cease to exist and the treatment rooms appear to flow into a sauna and candle-lit hammam – both glimmering dens of soothing curvilinear surfaces; timeless retreats from the sun-drenched world outside.

QUINTESSENTIALLY INSIDER
For a private spa experience book the Royal Dome Spa Villa, the most exclusive accommodation at the resort. With panoramic views and a stunning designed swimming pool, it also boasts an outdoor Jacuzzi, indoor and outdoor treatment areas and a sauna.

SANDA Spa, Hillside Su, Konyaaltı, Antalya, Turkey
Tel: +90 242 249 0700 Fax: +90 242 249 0707 Email: su@hillside.com.tr Web: www.hillsidesu.com

Antalya | Turkey

SANDA Spa

Everything about the 1960's inspired Hillside Su on the shores of Antalya, south west Turkey, is stark white, from the walls to the furniture and even the staff uniforms. Yet surprisingly, for such a minimalist environment, the atmosphere is totally relaxed and laid-back. Maybe it's because of the red, yellow, green and blue neon lights that glow throughout the building, maybe it's the giant disco balls that hang in the foyer, or the smiling, friendly staff that give it a fabulously fun Hollywood feel. The hotel has been attracting the young, the hip, the wealthy and the hedonistic since 2003, they come to hang out on the great beach, by the impressively large pool or at the lively bar, and they recuperate in the world-class SANDA Spa. Like the rest of the hotel the spa is a blank canvas bathed in soothing candle light and scattered with deep red rose petals. A wide range of Balinese-inspired therapies are designed to suit each individual guest and various two-, three-, four- and six-day packages offer great value for money. The Turkish bath breaks the mould with grey walls and in the soporific recovery room contented, blissed-out spa-goers line the walls on rows of white beds with huge yielding pillows.

QUINTESSENTIALLY INSIDER
If you thought coffee was bad for you, think again, SANDA Spa's new BODYCOFFEE treatments channel the powerful effects of coffee to detoxify all areas of the body – great for combating cellulite.

ACKNOWLEDGEMENTS

This publication is the third edition of Quintessentially Pure. Putting this book together has been great fun and a true enjoyment. The success of Pure is due to the dedicated efforts of a talented team at Quintessentially Publishing. As always, thanks are due to several people in particular without whom this book would not have been such a great achievement. A special mention goes to our design team: Leanne Simpson, Sally Walker-Tayler and Laetitia De Clercq whose dedication and creative insights helped launch this incredible edition. Recognition also goes to: Christopher Rayner and Russell Bryan for their unwavering commitment and positive approach to the book; to Lois Crompton and Eleanor Horsey for their hard work and organization; to our editors, Carol Krosnar (who is editing this title for the third time), for her attention to detail and thoughtful editorial and to Michaela Taylor for her fresh and insightful approach to the Spa industry. Finally, Anton Mossa for his help and support. And last, but certainly not least, to the global Quintessentially team for their deep knowledge of their territories and their helpful advice throughout the project.

QUINTESSENTIALLY

Quintessentially is the world's leading private members' club and concierge service. With offices in almost every major city, we'll keep you on the inside track 24 hours a day, 365 days a year and provide you with a complete lifestyle management service, wherever you may be. A membership to Quintessentially will give you unrivalled access to a range of exclusive benefits, offers and experiences across the globe. Whether it's travel, restaurants, wine, art and above all service — we'll save you time and money so you can enjoy the finer things in life.

Life is easier with a membership to Quintessentially.

To join us, call +44 (0)870 850 8585
www.quintessentially.com

ABIDJAN | ABU DHABI | ATHENS | BAHRAIN | BANGKOK | BARBADOS | BEIJING | BEIRUT | BOGOTA | BRUSSELS | BUENOS AIRES | CAIRO | CAPE TOWN
CASABLANCA | COPENHAGEN | DUBAI | DUBLIN | GENEVA | HONG KONG | ISTANBUL | JEDDAH | JOHANNESBURG | KUWAIT | LAGOS | LONDON | LOS ANGELES
MAPUTO | MEXICO CITY | MIAMI | MILAN | MOSCOW | NEW YORK | OSLO | PANAMA CITY | PARIS | SAN FRANCISO | SEOUL | SHANGHAI
SINGAPORE | ST JULIANS | STOCKHOLM | SYDNEY | TOKYO | VIENNA